Reptiles

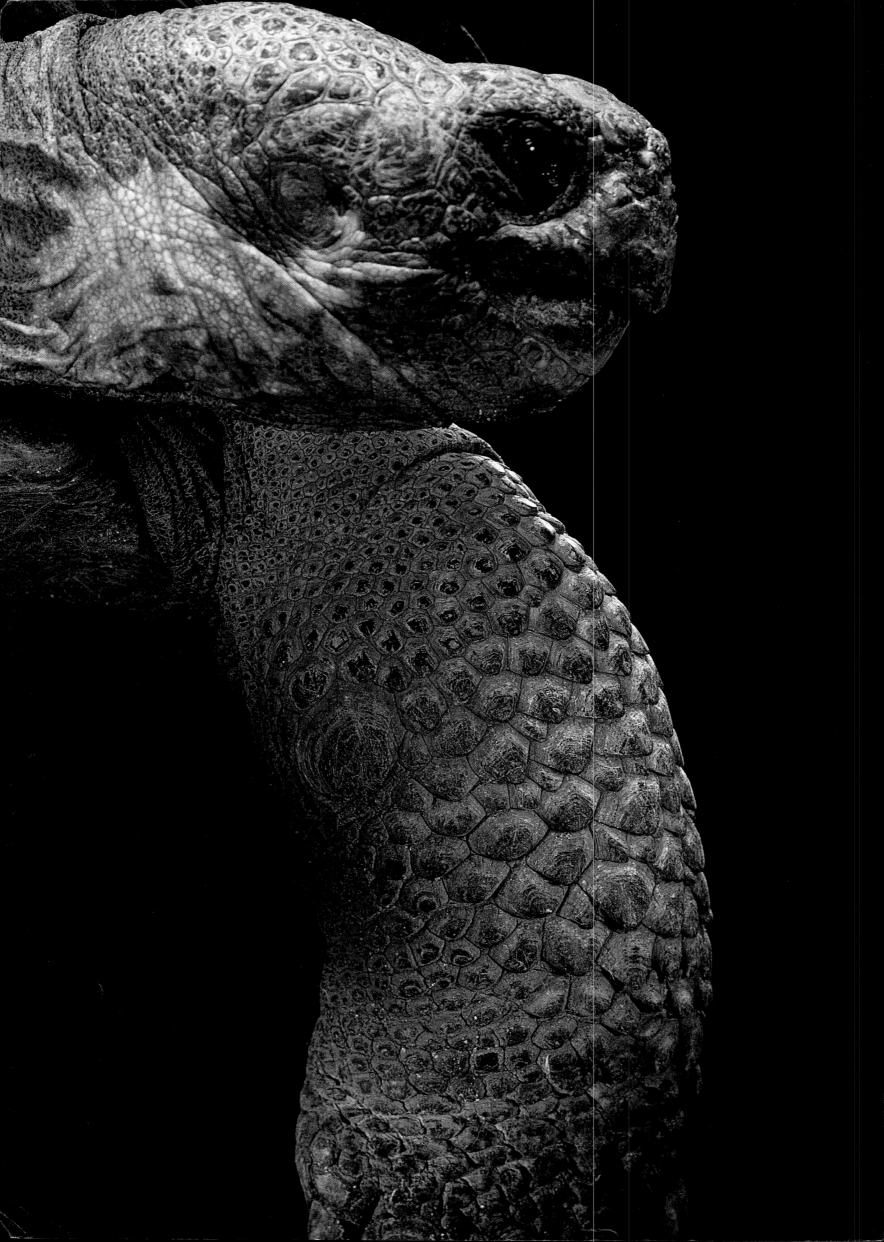

Reptiles

Photography by Paul Starosta

Written by Teddy Moncuit and Karim Daoues

BARNES
&NOBLE
BOOKS
NEW YORK

Contents

Photographing a reptile...

The first thing that springs to mind when asked to photograph a reptile is how to stop it from escaping. Little do you know that your problems have only just begun.

Place a lizard or a snake on a table under the lights and it will spend the entire time trying to escape. All you can do is be patient. The reptile meanwhile looks as though the only thing it regrets in life is not having been born with wings. It is only then that you realize what an ordeal this experience is for such a creature.

The reptile's reaction is to be expected but it is important not to make matters worse – both out of respect for the animal and for the ultimate success of the photograph. We once knew a cobra, for instance, who used to thwack the glass of its terrarium as you passed by. All trace of this proud behavior would vanish the minute you placed it on the table when suddenly all it could think about was escape.

It goes without saying that only an experienced handler can photograph venomous snakes or "close in" on a crocodile and bring it back to the studio. Several handlers are required when photographing sinewy snakes several feet long that you ask as nicely as possible to coil up in front of the camera, knowing full well that they have an unpleasant disposition and are certain to make a run for it at the first opportunity – but not before biting two or three people on the way and relieving themselves all over the place.

So you can imagine how much patience and skill it took to produce this book and how stressful it was, not only for the "models" but also for the photographer. It is a harrowing experience to stand within spitting distance of a viper as big as your arm that hisses furiously as it prepares to attack – and that could bite you before you know it. But so too is placing a gavial under the lights, a priceless and unique creature that is known to have a weak heart and skin so fine you could rip it with your fingernail – the nervous strain is unbearable.

But all's well that ends well. Out of the 200 animals we handled, only one small lizard lost its tail (now grown back again).

Whatever the problems they caused, these fascinating, magnificent, sculptural creatures rewarded our efforts a hundred times over.

Paul Starosta

Scales and cold-blood

What is the simplest way to define reptiles? Merely to say that they are cold-blooded, squamous (scaly) vertebrates is to ignore the extraordinary diversity of an ancient animal family that in the course of evolution has adapted to every kind of habitat: terrestrial, arboreal, fossorial (below ground), aquatic and marine.

There are currently more than 7,000 species of reptiles living in every corner of the globe with the exception of the polar zones. It is in hot climates however that they have really flourished and developed a variety of features – horns, crests, spines, claws – worthy of their prehistoric cousins.

Survivors of the Jurassic Period

They may look like diminutive prehistoric monsters but reptiles are not in fact descended from the dinosaurs, although they do have a common ancestor. The first reptilian forms appeared when terrestrial animals started to evolve and, thanks to the same evolutionary process, rapidly developed into the largest animals ever to have walked the face of the earth. The golden age of the legendary dinosaurs, rightly known as the "Age of Reptiles" was from the Jurassic to the Cretaceous Periods. Dinosaurs ruled the world for around 140 million years then abruptly disappeared some 65 million years ago together with many other large species when the climate suddenly changed. For some reason, part of the species escaped this wholesale extinction, perhaps because their aquatic or fossorial lifestyles made them less vulnerable to environmental upheaval.

Armor-plated scales

A reptile's skin is made up of overlapping scales that are part of the dermis. Unlike fish scales, which are separate and detachable, reptile scales cannot be rubbed off. Contrary to popular belief and also unlike fish, reptiles secrete no slime but are characteristically dry and sometimes rough to the touch.

The skin is composed of several layers of keratin and does not grow with the animal. Reptiles therefore have to change their skin throughout their lifetime, a process known as shedding.

The skin may be shed all at once (snakes), bit by bit (lizards) or progressively through wear and tear (tortoises and crocodiles).

Although their skin is often dull-colored for the sake of camouflage, reptiles have the ability to change color and adopt various colorations. Bright colors are due to combinations of various pigments in different layers of the skin. The skin

is protected and stiffened by bony plates beneath the scales called osteoderms. These are more pronounced in lizards and especially crocodiles, and serve as a form of subcutaneous armor.

Reptiles continue to grow throughout their lifetime although growth slows down dramatically once they reach sexual maturity. Within the same species the bigger the reptile, the greater its age. Life expectancy indeed is probably higher than for any other group of animals on earth: 40 to 50 years for the oldest lizards and snakes, 100 years for crocodiles and as long as 150 years for tortoises.

Not as cold-blooded as you might think

Reptiles are physiologically incapable of maintaining body temperature at a constant level, a primordial feature that determines much of their behavior. To describe them as "cold blooded" however is not entirely accurate.

Actually, reptiles are ectothermic: they rely on external sources of heat to maintain their body temperature and that in turn affects their level of activity. Heat passes through the bloodstream from the outer body that collects heat from the sun to the reptile's inner organs.

In contrast to mammals and birds, reptiles do not have to use a great deal of energy just to keep warm. As a result they need less food and can survive in harsh environments unsuitable for other forms of animal.

However, when the temperature no longer suits them, reptiles have no choice but to hibernate or aestivate, and their capacity for hibernation is truly astounding. We know of a researcher who decided to freeze to death a group of lizards that he wanted to dissect. Imagine his surprise when they all came back to life once removed from the freezer.

Reproductive strategies

Reptiles reproduce in all sorts of ways but mainly by laying eggs in warm, humid environments and leaving them to incubate. They occasionally lay in sand or termite hills for the sake of the heat-retaining properties in such locations. Crocodiles, a few snakes and one species of tortoise are the only reptiles that actually look after their nest, by adding plants that decompose and so produce the heat necessary for incubation. Other reptiles solve the incubation problem by bringing their eggs to term inside the oviducts and laying them only when the young are ready to hatch. There are even reptiles that give birth to live young. This method of reproduction is especially common in coastal or mountainous regions where weather conditions do not favor incubation.

● **Previous double-page display** *Python regius* [Ball Python – melanistic] **Details page 145**
● **Top left** *Chamaeleo Triceros johnston* [Johnston's Chameleon] shedding its skin **Details page 46**
● **Above** *Chamaeleo oustaletti* (young) **Details page 79**

An astonishing organ

With the exception of tortoises, which are toothless, and poisonous snakes, which have fangs, all reptiles have identical teeth that are regularly renewed (although not all at the same time). They also have good vision and hearing thanks to eardrums at the surface (except for snakes; they have no eardrums at all).

The most astonishing reptilian feature however, common to snakes and lizards alike, is a special organ of smell (and taste) in the palate called "Jacobson's Organ."

Whenever reptiles flick their tongues they pick up "chemical cues" in the air, which are then transferred to this special organ for analysis. Smell is their most highly developed sense. It allows them to communicate with other reptiles by means of these chemical cues, to locate prey or to identify intruders.

Tactics and defense mechanisms

Reptiles deploy a wide range of defense mechanisms of which the most obvious is snake venom and the chief and most important is mimicry. After all, the best way to avoid danger is not to be seen in the first place. Their colors and shapes are therefore designed to imitate their surroundings and even their movements can be a means of camouflage. Chameleons, for instance, advance in a jolting manner like a leaf blowing around in the wind.

Imitation is also a good means of defense. By turning the same color as more dangerous species, harmless reptiles stand a good chance of being avoided. This is a strategy used by American snakes that mimic the red, black and white markings of the highly venomous Coral Snake. Reptiles are also known to play dead. The Ringneck Snake for instance simply lies on its side with its mouth open and its tongue hanging out until the coast is clear.

Other defense mechanisms include an original if deliberately disgusting tactic used by a number of snakes and tortoises that spew up the entire contents of their cloaca. Lizards throw their assailant off course by sacrificing that non-vital organ, their tail, which is disconcerting to say the least.

With or without venom

Snakebites are as much a defense mechanism as a deterrent. Often used as a last resort, they serve as a stinging reminder of a nasty encounter. When disturbed, some snakes almost never bite but go into a threat display, seeking to frighten off the intruder rather than attack.

So what exactly is venom? It is a substance secreted by special salivary glands found in many snakes and two species of Mexican lizard.

Its primary function – whatever its other uses – is alimentary although it also serves to capture and kill prey, commence digestion by breaking down tissues through chemical action, and if necessary, also serves as a defense mechanism.

Three types of envenomating apparatus have been identified in snakes depending on the position of the fangs and whether they are mobile or fixed. Like other teeth, fangs are renewed throughout the snake's lifetime. The venom they secrete is a complex mixture of proteins, toxins and enzymes that act directly on cells and tissues, produce an inflammatory reaction or affect the nervous system and even the blood circulation. Venomous snakebites vary in effect from one species to another, one person to another and one bite to another. Snakes may also strike as a warning but withhold their venom, preferring not to waste the precious liquid. Such bites are known as "dry bites."

Above left *Two gecko eggs Phelsuma ornata* **Details page 79**
Above *Gonyosoma oxycephala* **Details page 108**

Bad Press

Reptiles with their prehistoric appearance and bizarre way of moving, have inspired countless myths and continue to exert a unique fascination.

Crocodiles, monitors, pythons and anacondas have all caught the imagination of primitive peoples and given rise to as many beliefs as there are cultures.

In the Judeo-Christian culture, the snake is the personification of evil because it was the serpent that tempted Eve to eat the forbidden fruit. Underlying this cultural context is our own ignorance that makes us fear snakes before we know anything about them. Contrast this with India where far from inspiring loathing some snakes are regarded as benign divinities.

Reptiles: an endangered species

Unlike pandas, reptiles do not have an endearing public image and are not as easy to protect.

As is often the case, the primary cause of their disappearance is the gradual depletion and destruction of their natural habitat. Over the past centuries about 100 species have already disappeared as a direct or indirect consequence of human intervention. In the 17th century for instance, there were still giant land tortoises in Mauritius (and Reunion Island) where man was busy wiping out the island's most famous one-time resident, the dodo. In the West Indies the local fauna has changed dramatically since men introduced mammals – rats, goats, rabbits and the mongoose – that now occupy habitats previously reserved for reptiles. Another ecological disaster in the making was the introduction of bullfrogs as a means of keeping down insect populations in sugar plantations. As toxic as they are prolific and with no natural enemies, the newcomers rapidly put the entire ecosystem in jeopardy.

Fashion has a lot to answer for

Man is also directly responsible for the rarefaction of the species. Excessive hunting nearly wiped out countless species of crocodile and to this day millions of pythons, monitor and tegu lizards finish up as boxes, boots and other fashion accessories.

Where they are not hunted for their skin, reptiles are hunted for their flesh, especially by rural communities. Caimans are considered a delicacy in Guyana where they are made into stews; tortoises, a traditional Chinese dish for hundreds of years, are on the verge of extinction in many parts of Asia.

The trade in live reptiles for pet stores, although in theory controlled, may also threaten the survival of certain groups. Then there is wanton destruction - the reptiles that are deliberately killed out of fear or ignorance – and accidental destruction - the snakes that finish under the wheels of a car or a truck. They may well be a protected species but nobody gives them a second thought.

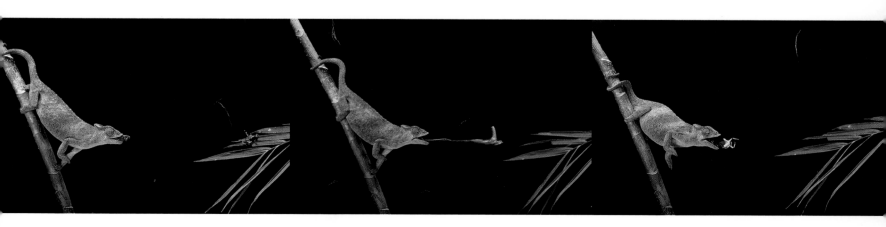

● **Above left** *Naja pallida* [Red Spitting Cobra] spitting venom **Details page 124**
● **Above** *Chameleon johnstoni* [Johnston's chameleon] **Details page 46**

Breeding as a means of conservation

The only real change in reptile conservation has resulted from financial incentives, legislation having proved largely ineffective. Crocodile breeding, for instance, has emerged as the only means to satisfy the needs of the leather industry without driving many species to the verge of extinction. Now regarded as one of the best examples of conservation, it combines the survival of the species with business interests.

On a lesser scale, breeding in captivity has led to a considerable reduction in the trade in wild animals. Large numbers of snakes, tortoises and lizards are now only available from breeders, thus avoiding the need to deplete populations in the wild.

In some cases, either because their original habitat no longer exists or because they are irretrievably doomed to extinction, the survival of a species actually depends on breeding.

A one-sided relationship

Whether you love them or loathe them, you are bound to feel something about reptiles. Reptile enthusiasts usually love them to distraction.

This neglected group of animals has a following of devotees ranging from amateur herpetologists to professional breeders. The feeling is not mutual however: reptiles do not respond to attention and rearing them in captivity is nothing like keeping a pet. Satisfaction instead comes from the pleasures of observation, from enriching your knowledge of the natural world or recreating a little corner of the wild. Terrariums are by no means as popular as aquariums but herpetology is becoming increasingly affordable. Advances in technology have made it possible to raise the vast majority of species in closed environments without adversely affecting their natural habitat. Dedicated amateur herpetologists may now observe these animals in captivity as never before, producing a steady stream of findings that significantly increase scientific understanding of reptilian biology and ethology.

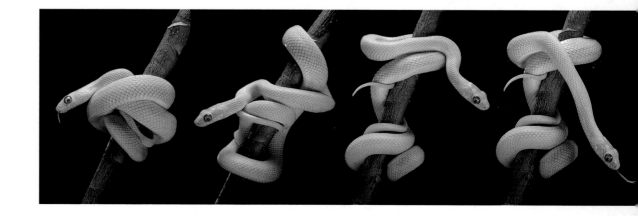

● **Left** *Acanthosaura armata* [Mountain Horn-headed Lizard] **Details page 78**
● **Above** *Elaphe obsoletta lindheimeri* f. *Leucistic* **Details page 145**

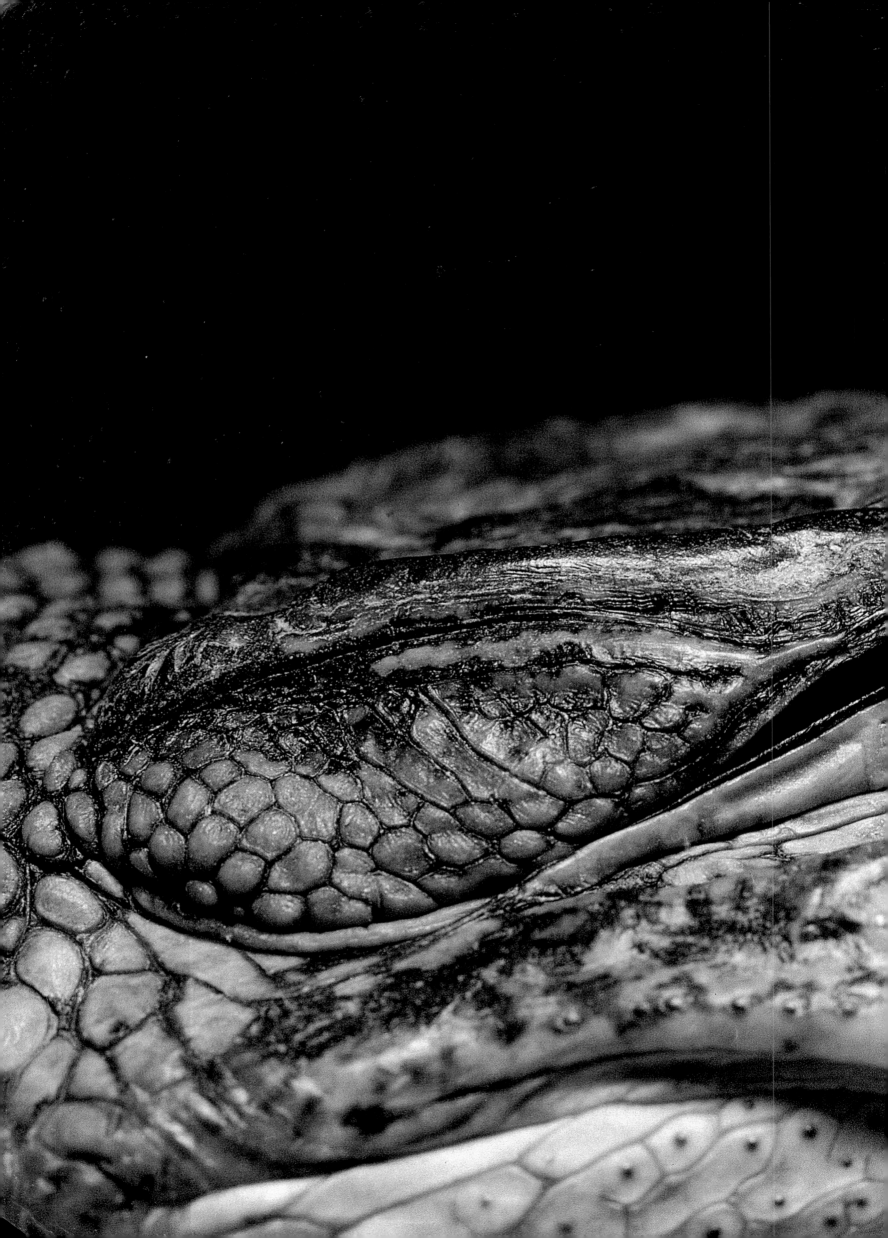

Crocodiles

These huge, prehistoric-looking predators emerged from the primordial slime in the same period as the dinosaurs. Crocodiles are highly evolved reptiles that communicate among themselves using a range of vocalizations, gurgles, roars and head movements.

Once a year, certain species of crocodiles build nests of leaves and plant debris in which to incubate their eggs (usually about 15-90). The female sits on the nest for two to three months, fiercely repelling any intruders. Incredibly, when the eggs are about to hatch, the babies in the shell call out to their mother who uncovers the nest, helps her young to hatch and escorts them to the water. And so begin many months of devoted protection.

All crocodiles have a similar morphology, reflecting how perfectly they have adapted to their aquatic environment. They can see under water thanks to an extra eyelid and can dive without risk of drowning thanks to special valves in their throat and nostrils. When lying in wait for prey, only the crocodile's eyes and nostrils are visible above the surface of the water.

Crocodiles are cumbersome on dry land but in the water their armor-plated jaws and infinite patience make them formidable hunters. They can overcome very large prey indeed although they are easily satisfied and need only a few meals a month.

Crocodiles are principally tropical creatures and are found in a variety of biotopes including major waterways, rivers, marshes, torrents, brackish waters and even the sea. Each species has its own particular preferences.

Crocodiles have been known to live for more than 80 years, but such veterans are rare these days, their numbers having been decimated in the 20th century by the excessive predations of the leather industry. Populations have now stabilized and are even expanding since the introduction of stringent wildlife protection legislation and the setting up of successful breeding programs.

Crocodilians all belong to the family Crocodylidae, a very homogeneous group that may be subdivided into three subfamilies: the Crocodilia, the Alligatoridae and the Gavialidae.

Previous double-page display: *Alligator mississibiensis* [American Alligator]. Details page 36

Alligatoridae

This subfamily composed of alligators and caimans includes eight species found throughout America and one in China. Three of these species live in temperate zones where the waters are likely to freeze in winter.

Alligators and caimans may be distinguished from crocodiles by the teeth in their lower jaw that fit into small cavities on the upper jaw, so becoming invisible when the reptile closes its mouth.

The Narrow-snouted Spectacles Caiman owes its name to the bony ridge over its eyes that makes it look as though it is wearing spectacles.

It is the most common and widespread of the South American crocodiles and likely to supplant other, more widely hunted species. It adjusts well to the company of man and may be seen near houses and fields, in ponds for livestock, ditches and dams. It is also farmed and, like other species, attracts the unwanted attentions of the leather industry.

Caiman crocodilus
[Narrow-snouted Spectacles Caiman]

Distribution
Southern Mexico to northern Argentina. Introduced by man to southern Florida and the Isle of Pines, off Cuba

Average size
6.5ft., rarely more than 8ft.

Breeding details
Occasionally reared in captivity because of its small size, although not suitable for terrariums

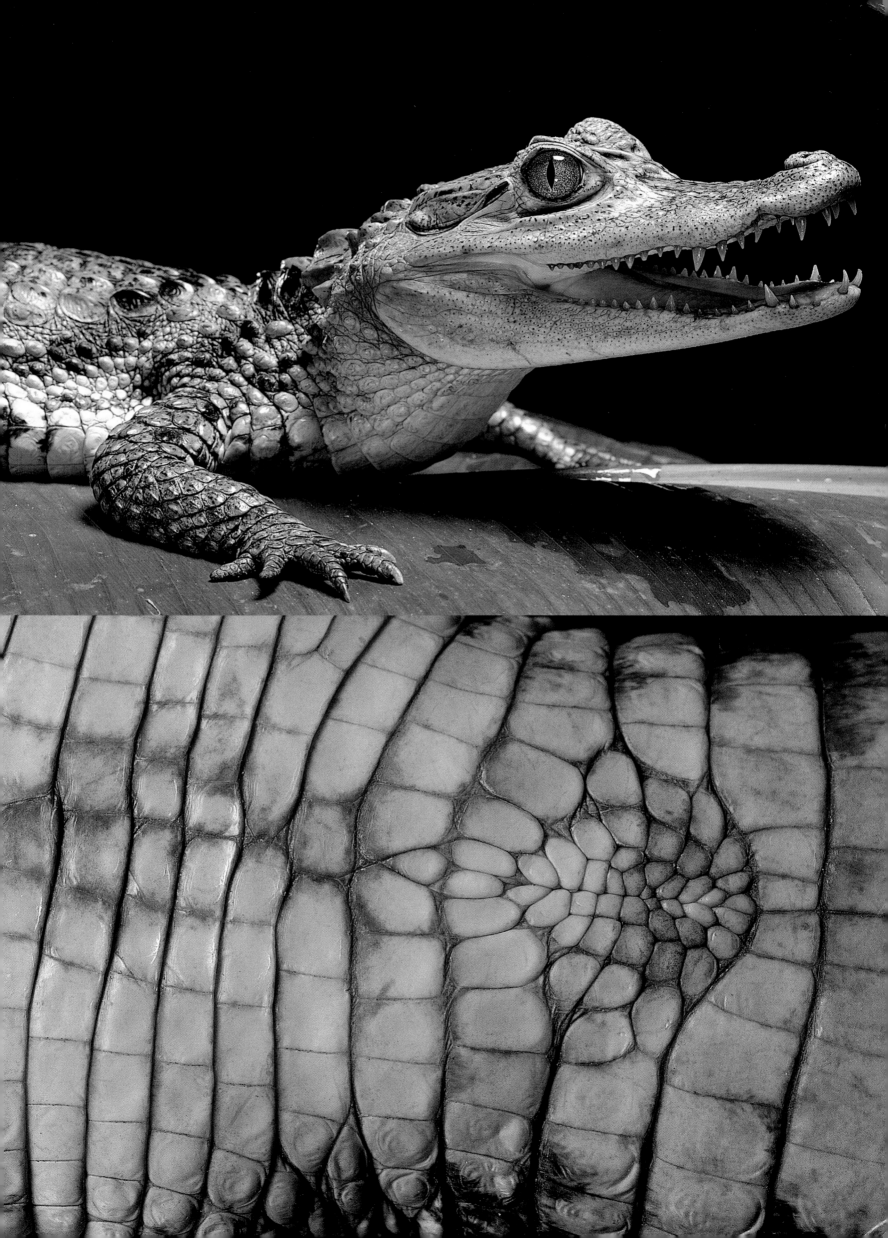

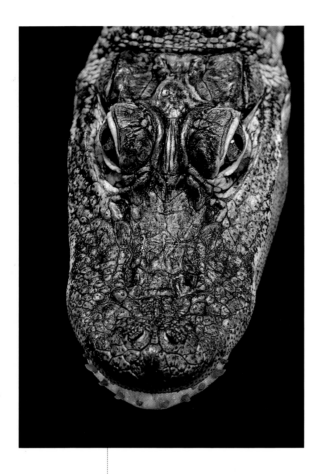

The Chinese Alligator
that inspired the
fabled Chinese
dragon is a rapidly vanishing
species. At the point of writing, it
has virtually disappeared from its
last natural habitat in China where it
was previously found in rivers,
marshes and ponds. It was also a
frequent lodger in caves and
burrows where it spent the winter
months from October to March.

Alligator sinensis
[Chinese Alligator]

Distribution
*Now restricted
to ponds on the lower
reaches of the Yangtze Kiang*

Average size
5–6.5ft.

Breeding details
*Occasionally raised in
Germany by reptile lovers
belonging to societies
for the protection of
endangered species*

Pages 18-19

The American Alligator,
emblem of Florida
where it is now a star,
forms part of the history of the
American people. Life is kinder these
days to this 13ft. giant that was
persecuted until 1969, when hunting
was outlawed. The opening of crocodile
farms, national parks and wildlife
reserves has been so successful that it
is not uncommon now to see one
sheltering from the sun under a car in a
parking lot or taking a dip in one of the
many privately owned pools.

Alligator mississippiensis
[American Alligator]

Distribution
*From North Carolina
to Florida, Louisiana
and Texas*

Average size
10–13ft.

Breeding details
*Traditionally captured
as a pet, the American
Alligator is now spared
man's attentions and
confined to wildlife reserves*

Crocodylidae

This subfamily includes the real giants, crocodiles as we imagine them and the most typical of the order. They are characterized by notches in the jaw into which the teeth are fitted, the teeth always remaining visible. The fourth tooth on the lower jaw is especially large and juts out slightly even when the animal has its mouth closed.

The 13 species of Crocodylidae are distributed across all of the continents except for Europe and live almost exclusively in tropical zones.

The quality of its skin is the principal reason for this crocodile's disappearance

from Central America, where it is increasingly under threat of extinction because of the difficulty of enforcing the legislation that protects it. The shy Morelet's Crocodile prefers soft water in remote places, such as streams and dead channels in the depth of the forest, or estuaries and lagoons in coastal regions. It feeds on small aquatic vertebrates and small mammals, fish, crabs, reptiles and birds.

Crocodylus moreleti
[Morelet's Crocodile]

Distribution
*Mexico, Belize
and Guatemala*

Average size
6.5–8ft.

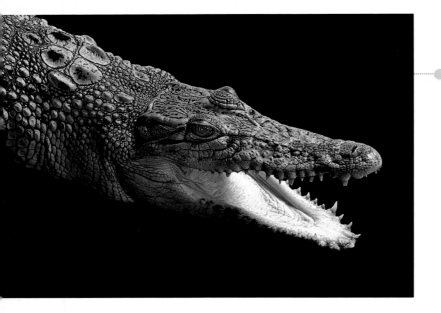

This man-eater can grow to 23ft. in length

and may weigh nearly a ton. The biggest and largest of all the crocodiles, the Saltwater Crocodile thinks nothing of traveling long distances by sea, which explains its widespread distribution. As much at home in soft water as in brackish or salt water, it has a very varied diet that occasionally includes man - hence the presence in Australia of signs forbidding swimming near watering holes where it is likely to be lurking.

Crocodylus porosus
[Saltwater Crocodile]

Distribution
*The entire Indo–Pacific region including
northern Australia and the South
(and Central) Pacific islands (but no
longer present in the Seychelles)*

Average size
13–16ft.

Following double-page illustration *Crocodylus niloticus* [East African Nile Crocodile] **Details page 32**

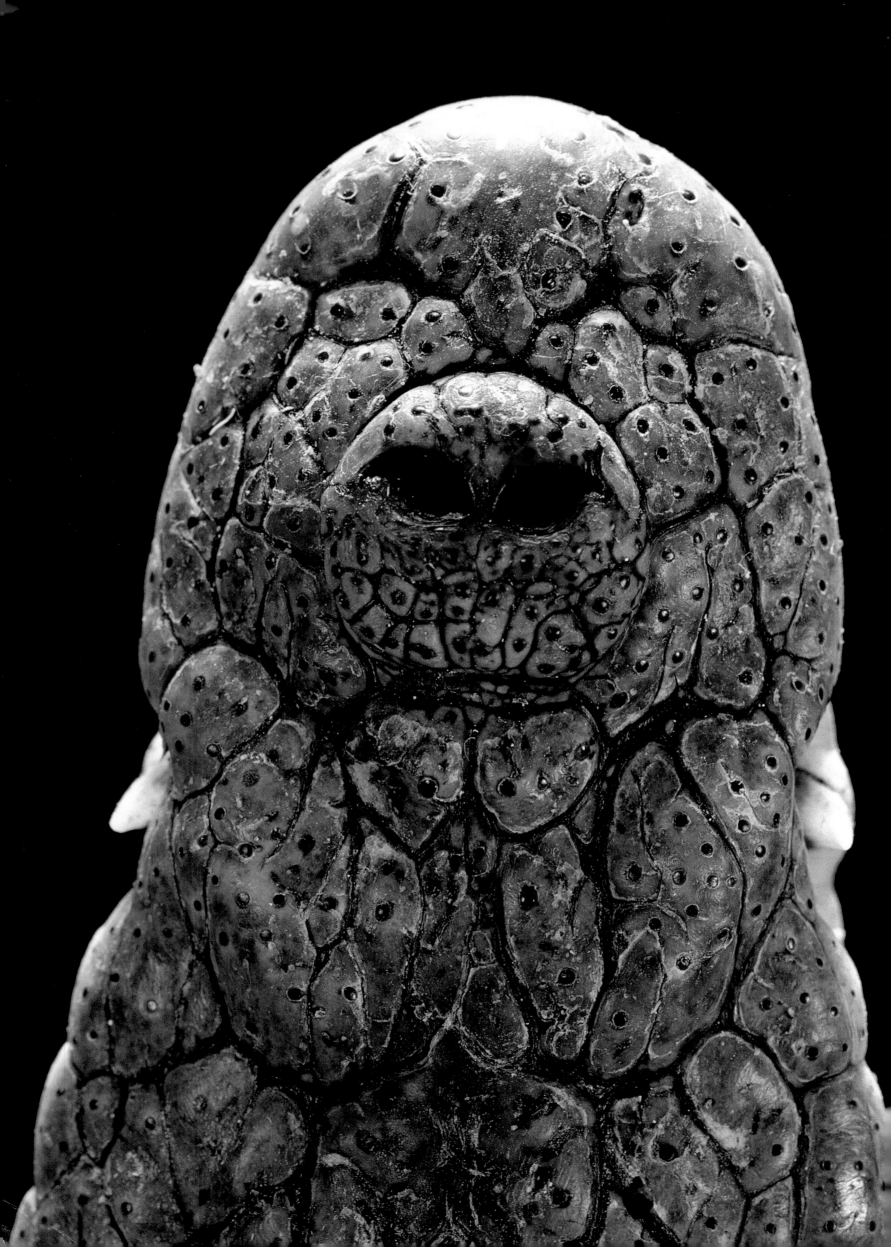

Previous double-page display ● ●

This ancient Egyptian God that was worshipped by the Pharaohs is part of daily life for the people of Africa. Adored, feared and hunted, it is the leather industry's favorite and now bred for its skin as well as its flesh. In the wild, it lives in a range of habitats from desert pools to lagoons, marshes and woodland rivers. The young survive on insects and amphibians but adults occasionally feast off antelope, wildebeest and zebras.

Crocodylus niloticus
[East African Nile Crocodile]

Distribution
Throughout tropical and southern African, Madagascar and Egypt
Average size
10-16ft. (maximum 20ft.)

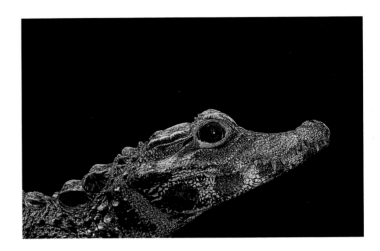

This discreet resident of the dense African equatorial forests is the smallest of all the crocodiles and also the most terrestrial. It is occasionally seen at night, on dry land miles from the tranquil rivers that it prefers. Thanks to a skin that is rich in bony scales called osteoderms, the Dwarf Crocodile does not arouse the greed of the leather industry.

Osteolaemus tetraspis
[West African Dwarf Crocodile]

Distribution
West and Central Africa to Angola, south of the Gulf of Guinea
Average size
9ft.
Breeding details
Although very small for a crocodile, it is still only bred by specialists.

Following double-page display ●

Man's increasing presence is a disaster

for this little known, shy crocodile that becomes extremely distressed when disturbed, usually scuttling off into the vegetation rather than diving under water. Its favorite habitats are tropical lagoons where it mainly feeds off fish but is not averse to other prey. This African species of gavial bears a resemblance to its Indian relative and is similarly enigmatic.

Crocodylus cataphractus
[African Slender-snout Crocodile]

Distribution
From Senegal to Angola
Average size
6.5-10ft.

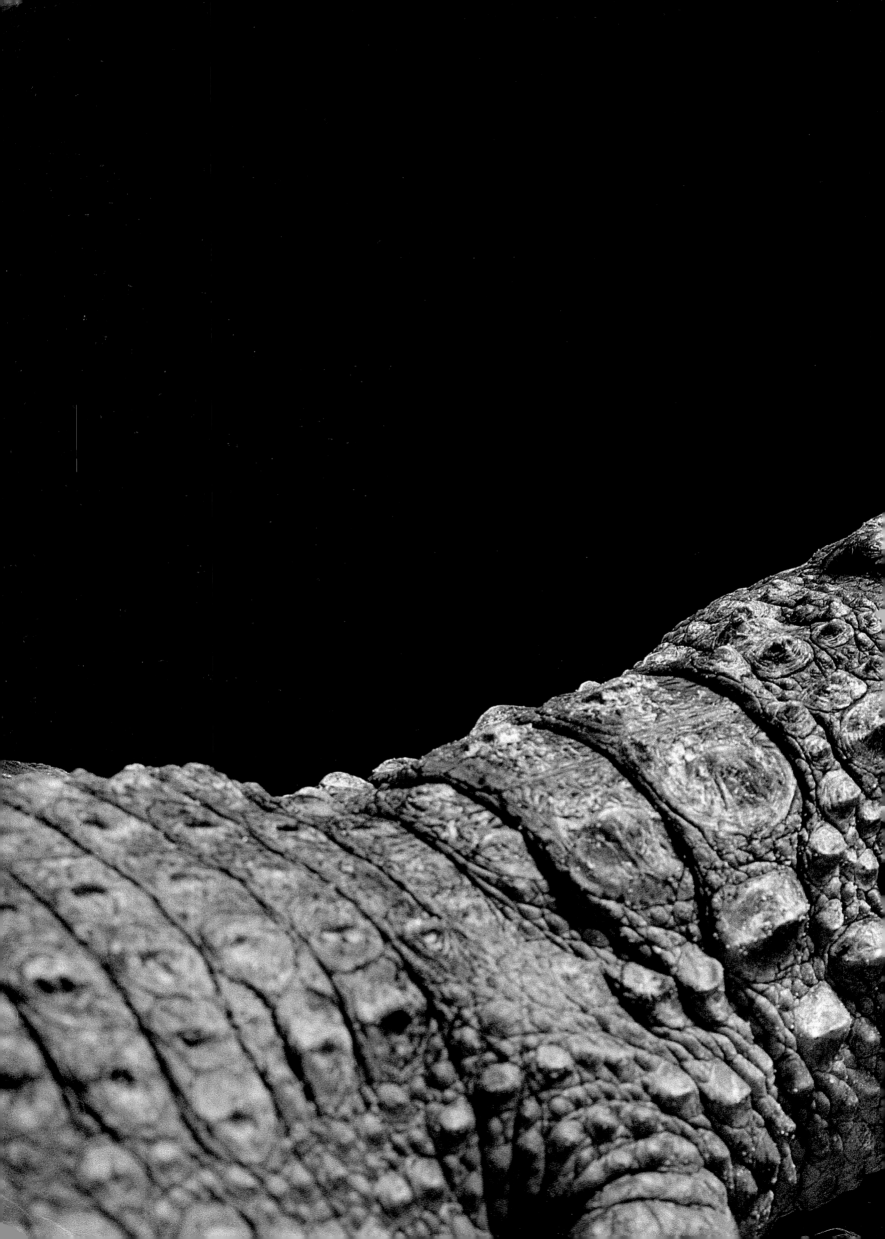

Gavialidae

The strangest and rarest of the Crocodylidae, as well as the most aquatic, are confined to Asia. The Gavialidae subfamily consists of just two species that have developed a characteristically narrow snout to suit their fish-eating diet. Despite their large size, they never attack man.

It is a miracle that this relic of the Jurassic Period, unique of its kind, survived the 20th century and near-extinction in the 1970s. Although its future remains precarious a breeding program in Nepal aims to reintroduce the Garial to its natural habitat. In India, Garials were traditionally regarded as man-eaters because they fed off the corpses that floated down river after funerals. In fact, for all its small, sharp teeth, the snout is too long and narrow to deal with anything but fish and amphibians.

Gavialis gangeticus
[Garial]

Distribution
India, Nepal and Bangladesh
(but probably extinct in Pakistan)

Average size
13–16.5ft.
(but occasionally more than 20ft.)

Breeding details
France is the only country in
Europe where Gharials can
be seen in captivity. The group
at the "Ferme aux Crocodiles"
in Pierrelatte (in the Drôme)
was a gift from the King of
Nepal and were bred in captivity.

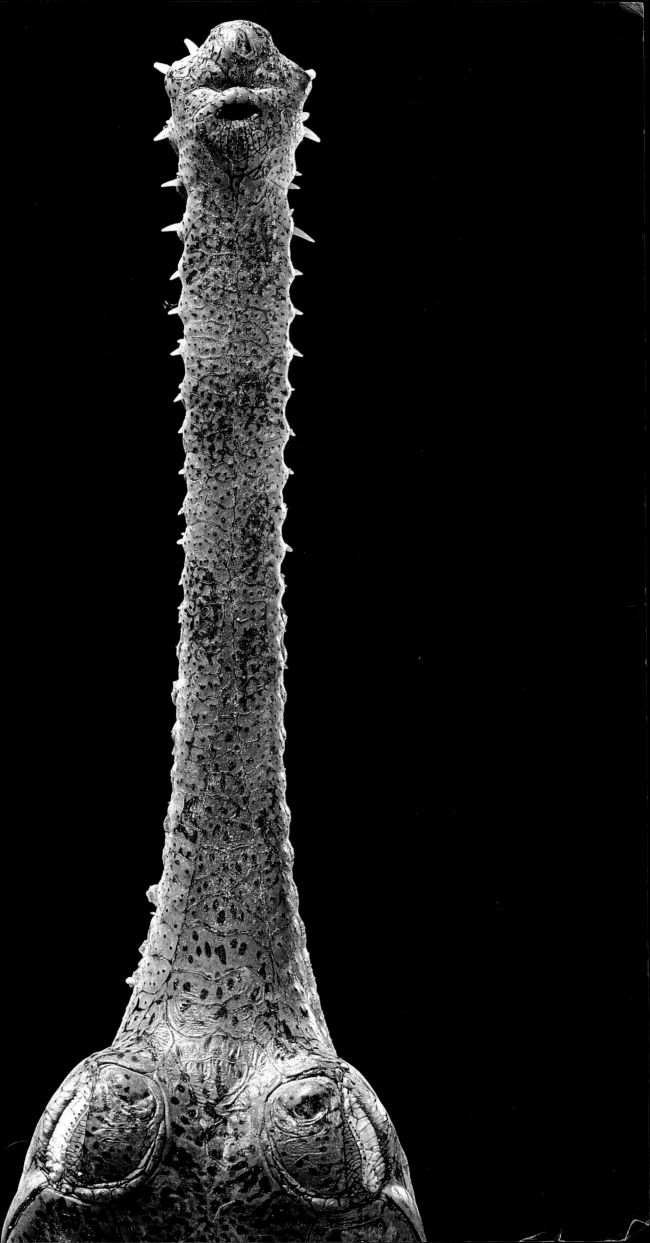

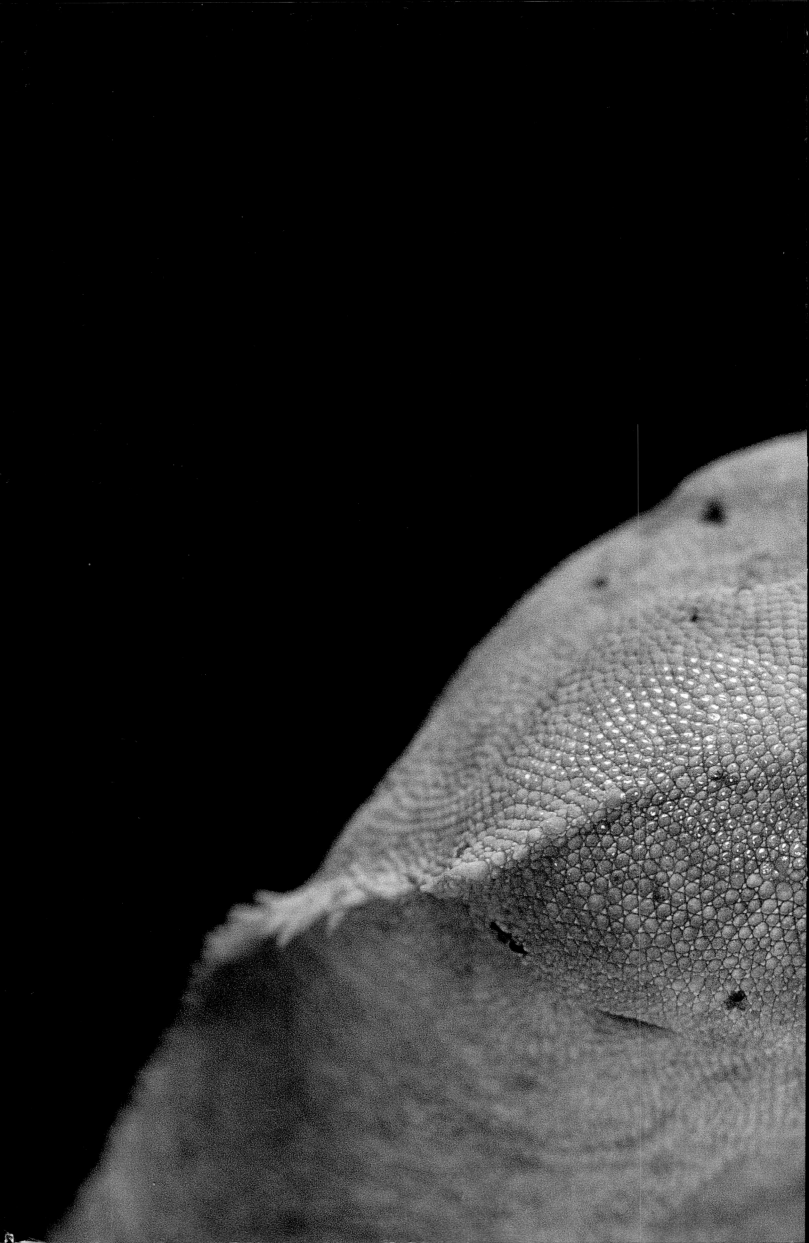

Lizards are the most common of all the reptiles, found in every continent except Antarctica and a few Arctic regions. There are more than 3,800 known species and new species are discovered every year. Lizards in hot countries are very varied, usually small in size and confined to one particular type of habitat (clump of grass, cave, canopy of foliage, bark of a particular tree). In Cuba, for example, the same tree is home to as many as three different species of anole, each with its own territory at a certain level up the height of the tree. The lizard's adaptability has led to the emergence of many different species including some that are restricted to one particular area.

In terms of habitat, lizards are even more ubiquitous than snakes and are found in a variety of environments from the middle ranges of the Himalayas to the coastal regions of the Galapagos Islands. Size and life-span are equally variable: from less than one inch long with a life-expectancy of a few years at most to very large indeed and capable of living for several decades. There is a case of a slow worm that lived for more than 50 years.

Camouflage and escape are the lizard's most common defense mechanisms although large species are quick to confront attackers when cornered.

The only venomous lizards are the Heloderms that secrete poison from glands in their lower jaw, gradually poisoning the hapless victim with every leisurely chew. Their unique ability however, is not so much an aid to digestion as a form of defense.

All lizards possess very good hearing and excellent sight but in all other respects their anatomy is as varied as their lifestyles. The tail usually plays an important role, whether as a reserve of fat when times are lean, as an extra limb (invaluable to arboreal species) or sometimes as a defense mechanism. Some species are by stages evolving without legs – skinks for instance. Others have already lost them, like the Anguid lizards, the Slow Worm family and the American Slender Glass Lizard. The latter owes its name to a defense mechanism that is common among lizards: caudal autonomy or the deliberate shedding of a non-vital part of the tail.

Male lizards are territorial and aggressive as well as being bigger, brighter, more decorative and more active than the females. Most lizards are oviparous and generally leave it to Nature and the sun to take care of their eggs.

● **Previous double-page display** *Rhacodactylus ciliatus* [Eyelash Gecko] **Details page 80**
● **Left** *Sceloporus malachiticus* [Green Spiny Lizard] **Details page 60**

Agamidae

There are more than 320 species of agamids inhabiting a wide range of biotopes in warm regions of the Old World (Africa and Asia) and Australia. There is also a species of agamid living in southern Europe.

The Agamidae are distinguished by their acrodont teeth: rootless teeth that are fused at the base to the margin of the jawbones. These lizards also often display crests, spikes and other appendages that are designed to make them look impressive.

Some agamids grow to be very large – Hydrosaurus weberi or Chlamidosaurus kingrii, for example, can be more than 3ft long. Apart from the large species (such as those occurring in desert habitats) which are partially or totally herbivorous, all agamids are insectivorous and voracious eaters. They are predominantly oviparous.

This spiny, brilliantly colored agamid only comes down to ground level to relieve itself. The rest of the time if lives aloft in 1,000 year-old trees in remote regions of the world. Despite its inoffensive appearance, it has a fierce temper and reveals a fine set of teeth when roused.

Gonocephalus chamaeleontinus

Distribution
Java and Sumatra
Average size
8–10in.

This is the smallest and most recently discovered of the seven known species of Pogona. It lives in a hilly region of black, semi-humid soil in a transitional desert zone scattered with thorn bushes. Its varied diet consists of insects, spiders and plants.

Pogona brevis
[Black-soil Plains
Bearded Dragon]
Distribution
Central and northwest
Queensland, Australia
Average size
3ft.
Breeding details
Easy — less cumbersome
than its close relatives

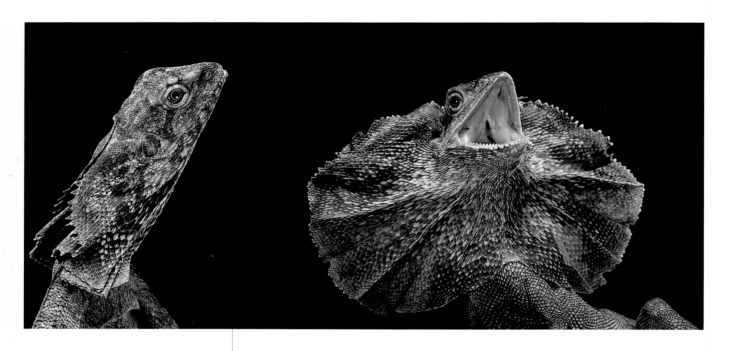

Despite looking like something from the Jurassic Period, this is not a 21st century dinosaur but a Frilled Dragon, a diurnal denizen of semi-humid wooded regions that spends most of its life on the lookout for intruders. Thanks to its unique make-up it always puts on an impressive show of aggression - splayed frill, sharp teeth, lashing tail, piercing whistles.

Chlamydosaurus kingii
[Frilled Dragon]

Distribution
*North and northwest Australia
and Papua New Guinea*
Average size
31–39in.
Breeding details
Now frequently bred in Europe

This fellow likes remote tropical forests at high altitude (up to 9,000ft) where, like its close relative G. chamaeleontinus (see previous page) it can hide from prying eyes. It is distinguished from the many other species of Gonocephalus by its dark green color and small size.

Gonocephalus kuhlii

Distribution
Java and Sumatra
Average size
6–7.5in.

Chamaeleonitidae

Acrobatic prowess makes chameleons the masters of their arboreal habitats. Widespread throughout the African Continent, these lizards are also present in India, the Middle East, Southern Europe and the islands of the Indian Ocean. Their extremely specialized body is perfectly adapted to life among the trees: opposable digits fused into pincers to grip branches; prehensile tail that serves as a fifth leg; eyes that rotate independently for 360° vision; protractile tongue (as long as the tail) to catch insects from a distance...

The chameleon's ability to change color is positively mesmerizing. In a matter of seconds, it can modify both its pattern and coloration, often communicating with other chameleons by the change in color. The males don vivid colors to woo the females, who turn a darker color when they are not inclined to mate.

Chameleons living at altitude in the African Mountains are usually viviparous but the others are all oviparous and lay their eggs in the ground (sometimes as many as 60 at a time).

Horns are a feature of males only, serving to
identify them and helping them to compete for females or territory. Johnston's Chameleon has adapted to the cool, windy, humid climate of tropical forests at high altitude (6,000 – 8,200ft) – unlike other chameleons, it dislikes heat. It is strictly insectivorous.

Chamaeleo (Trioceros) johnstoni
[Johnston's Chameleon]

Distribution
*Burundi, Rwanda, Uganda
and the borders of the
Democratic Republic of the Congo*

Average size
10in.

Breeding details
*Only for the most
experienced breeders*

This multicolored inhabitant of humid, tropical zones is famous for its.... aggressive behavior.

When disturbed, it launches into a firework display of color ranging from turquoise blue to bright green and adopts intimidating, dramatic postures. Its coat of many colors makes this genus one of the most beautiful of the species. Diet is very varied: insects, lizards, tiny mammals and, rarely, young chameleons and birds.

Furcifer (Chamaeleo) pardalis
[Panther Chameleon]

Distribution
*Madagascar, introduced
to Reunion Island*

Average size
16-20in.

Breeding details
*Prolific and fascinating,
but often aggressive*

Cordylidae

The Cordylidae are restricted to Black Africa and flourish in southern Africa in particular.

They are all diurnal and usually live amongst the rocks where they love to bask in the sun, scuttling into the smallest cracks and fissures at the first sign of trouble - they are constantly on the alert. Their strong, hard scales are arranged in rings around their body and frequently end in a sharp point. When threatened, Cordylus cataphractus rolls into a ball with its tail in its mouth so as to protect its vulnerable belly, the only part of its body that has no scales.

The Cordylidae family is composed of some 40 or so species, all viviparous with very few exceptions, and insectivorous. They are not prolific breeders but hatchlings are well developed, which improves their chances of survival. Those living in the southernmost regions of Africa are forced to hibernate.

This fascinating creature that looks like something straight out of legend is diurnal and terrestrial and lives in colonies in crowded burrows deep in the prairies. It spends its days on the lookout, basking in the sun on a mound of earth. Owing to the cold winters, it is inactive for much of the year. This species is threatened because it lives on agricultural land.

Cordylus giganteus
[Sungazer]

Distribution
South Africa

Average size
14 in.

Breeding details
Very robust but will only reproduce if kept in an outdoor terrarium

Gekkonidae

Geckos are champions of adaptability that have conquered almost every type of habitat. With more than 900 species, the Gekkonidae are the second largest family of lizards.

The majority of geckos are arboreal, dull colored and nocturnal but a few are diurnal and brightly colored. They are insectivorous and the diurnal varieties are very fond of nectar. The males are fiercely territorial, chasing away intruders with loud shrieks (rare for a reptile). In Asia the gecko's nocturnal chant is audible from a distance of more than 100 yards. Because their eyelids are fixed, geckos regularly flick their tongues to clean their eyes. The vast majority of geckos lay two eggs at a time although there are (rare) cases of viviparity. Man's presence promises an easy dinner for some varieties that prey on the insects attracted to outdoor lights.

One of the gecko's most astonishing features is its ability to scale any surface thanks to adhesive pads on its toes. Each pad is composed of hundreds of thousands of setae (microscopic foot-hairs) that blossom at the end into tiny split ends (spatulae). This increases surface contact allowing the gecko to climb rapidly up just about any vertical surface – including polished glass.

Village nights are punctuated by the vocalizations, barks and groans of this large, disgruntled character that is known to bite but is especially colorful with its vivid, predominantly blue and red coloring. Its voracious appetite leads it to hunt other lizards but also insects, tiny mammals and small snakes.

Gekko gecko
[Tokay Gecko]

Distribution
Pakistan to the Philippines and Indonesia; introduced to Hawaii and Florida

Average size
12–14in.

Breeding details
Easy to breed but aggressive and noisy with an insatiable appetite

Above, left *Eublepharis macularius* [Leopard Gecko], **right** *Eublepharis macularius* f. *albinos*
Following double-page illustration *Eublepharis macularius* f. *golden*

Details page 79

This gecko's bark-and-lichen coloring provide perfect camouflage against the tree-trunks on which it sleeps during the day. At nightfall, it slowly stirs itself into action, using its excellent nighttime vision to hunt insects. Despite its cryptic coloration, it takes no chances and moves cautiously.

Uroplatus henkeli
[Leaf-tailed Gecko]

Distribution
Madagascar

Average size
10in.

Breeding details
Easy to breed but the young often suffer from mineral deficiencies

The fat, truncated tail

is principally used to store fat but it also serves to fool predators who mistake it for the gecko's head. When attacked, the gecko sheds its fat tail and escapes, leaving its assailant busily occupied. The damaged lizard will have to wait several months for the precious tail to regenerate completely.

Hemitheconyx caudicinctus
[African Fat-tailed Gecko]

Distribution
West Africa from Senegal to Nigeria

Average size
6in.

Breeding details
Less sociable than the Leopard Gecko. Breeding has recently produced some spectacular color mutations

Bright spots or stripes on a florescent background, small gurgling vocalizations and the ability to climb virtually any surface are characteristics shared by the genus Phelsuma. These are the Day Geckos from the Mascarene Islands, without a doubt the most beautifully colored of all the lizards. Diurnal and arboreal, they like to bask in the sun on bushes, coconut palms or the walls of houses. They feed on insects and spiders but are also very fond of nectar and rotting fruit. They are very adaptable and occur in a variety of habitats ranging from humid tropical forests to dry, arid zones and even the outskirts of towns. Despite their retiring nature, Day Geckos are the subject of countless myths and legends. Local people believe that it brings bad luck to come across one and on some islands, they are even thought to be poisonous.

Phelsuma v−nigra

Distribution
Comoros

Average size
4in.

Breeding details
To avoid the risk of hybridization, it is important to separate specimens from different geographic origins

Iguanidae

These are probably the best known of all the lizards and appear to share the world with the Agamidae. According to a recent classification system, the Iguanidae family may be subdivided into eight close families although this new grouping is not accepted by all. Unlike the Agamidae, the iguana's teeth are planted on the inner margin of the jawbone; they are independent and will regenerate if lost.

Originally from the Americas, iguanas floated across the seas for months on makeshift rafts to the Galapagos Islands, Fiji and Tonga where they have been established for a very long time. Their presence in Madagascar, in the heart of agamid territory, remains a mystery although it probably predates the splitting of Gondwanaland (southern super-continent of the Paleozoic age) when the American continent was still connected to Madagascar.

This giant herbivore rules over an immense kingdom.

Semi- arboreal and diurnal, it often lives in the tree canopies of tropical forests although it increasingly flourishes in colonies on the outskirts of towns in South America.

Iguana iguana
[Common Iguana]

Distribution
Throughout Central and South America, from Mexico to Brazil; also in the Caribbean; introduced to Miami

Average size
4.5ft. (maximum 6ft.)

Breeding details
Frequently found in terrariums, bred by the thousand on specialized farms but often too large to be kept successfully in captivity

The impressive gular dewlap unfurls like a flag

at the approach of a female or rival. This anole, now one of the most common lizards in Florida where it was introduced 30 years ago, has always been an adept colonizer of new territories on the back of human migrations. It currently lives in a variety of biotopes including urban environments.

Anolis sagrei
[Brown Anole]

Distribution
Cuba, the Bahamas, Florida, Jamaica

Average size
8in.

Breeding details
Frequently sold but, strangely, rarely bred

Beware all rivals - this dominant male rules over several females.

The beautiful Asian Water Dragon, often confused with the Common Iguana, is arboreal, terrestrial and semi-aquatic, living in forested habitats by the water. A strong swimmer, it often perches on a low branch overhanging the water ready to dive in if threatened. Its very varied diet includes insects, tiny mammals, frogs, lizards and even ripe fruit.

Physignathus cocincinus
[Asian Water Dragon]

Distribution
*Vietnam, Thailand
and southeast China*

Average size
*20in. (females)
27in. (males)*

Breeding details
Prolific and easily bred

Perched on the lookout, ready to decamp at the first sign of danger, this

diurnal lizard likes open tropical forests in mountainous regions where it preys on insects and sometimes, smaller lizards. Like all iguanas, the males display vivid colors that serve to intimidate intruders and conquer females and territory – which usually involves a fierce battle.

Sceloporus malachiticus
[Green Spiny Lizard]

Distribution
*Southern Mexico
to Panama*

Average size
7in.

Breeding details
*Available from pet
stores although
rarely bred*

Following double-page illustration *Cyclura cornuta* [Rhinoceros Iguana] **Details page 81**

Lacertidae

The Lacertidae were the first lizards ever studied by scientists in the 18th century – among them Linnaeus in 1758.

Common throughout the whole of Europe (and right up to the Arctic Circle in the case of Lacerta vivipara) lacertids are most prevalent around the Mediterranean Basin. They are also well established in Africa and one particular group has even settled in Asia.

These are typical lizards as illustrated in any European or American schoolbook with no exceptional features: quadruped for speed, small in size, and with a tail that sheds when held.

All lacertids are insectivores although the type of insect eaten depends on the size of the lizard. They are predominantly terrestrial and spend a large part of their time basking in the sun or defending their tiny territory.

This lizard's incredibly long tail

(five times as long as its body) helps it to balance when leaping through the grass and bushes of the humid tropical savannah. Partly prehensile, the tail is of considerable assistance to the lizard's daily travels in search of insects. When threatened, it uses a strategy common to many lizards: caudal autonomy or the deliberate shedding of its tail that continues to lash about on the ground, so distracting the assailant's attention. It will take several months for the tail to regenerate completely.

Takydromus sexlineatus
[Longtail Lizard]

Distribution
South–East Asia

Average size
10–12in.

Breeding details
Docile and ideal in a community terrarium

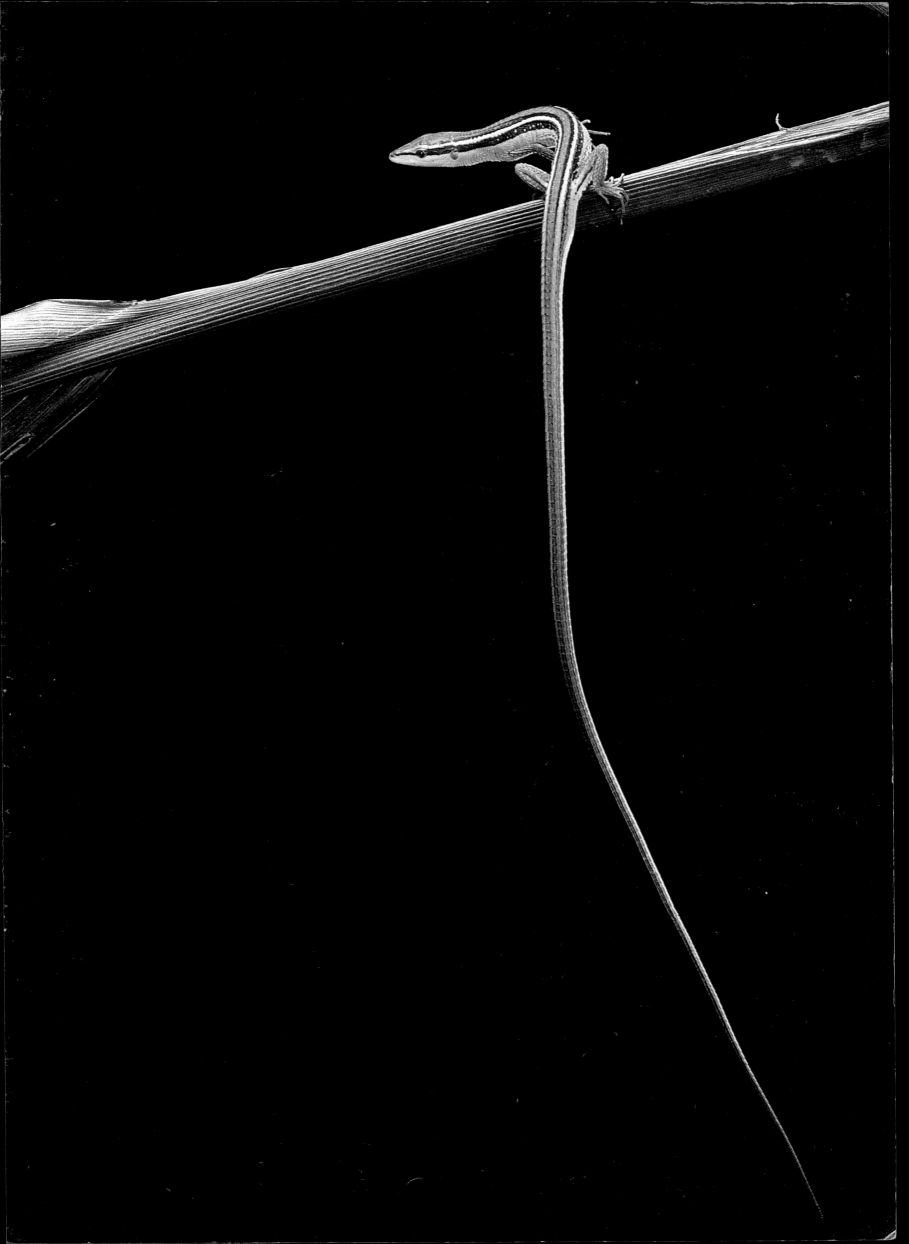

Pygopodidae

These close relatives of the geckos have almost lost their legs in the evolutionary process and now look more like snakes than lizards. The front legs have disappeared altogether and the only remaining traces of the back legs are two tiny appendages that are useful only for mating.

Found exclusively in Australia and New Guinea, pygopods are terrestrial or fossorial, occasionally occupying the burrows of spiders or rodents. They usually prey on spiders and insects although two species specialize in hunting lizards. Their fine, backward-sloping teeth are specially adapted to prevent smooth-scaled skinks from slipping free and the mobile front section of the skull ensures a perfect grip.

All pygopods are capable of vocalization but the Delma species has a defense mechanism of a special kind. When threatened, it leaps repeatedly into the air, balancing on its long tail and lunging in different directions until the bewildered aggressor eventually retreats.

This long lizard with its slender snout is often mistaken for a snake because only vestiges remain of its atrophied legs. It lives in very varied tropical habitats, occasionally in burrows and is partially diurnal, feeding exclusively on lizards and snakes that it captures thanks to sharp teeth that are partially articulated at the base. A great many lizards show a tendency to evolve with an extended body and diminished limbs or no limbs at all.

Lialis jicari
[New Guinea Legless Lizard]

Distribution
Papua New Guinea

Average size
16-20in.

Breeding details
*Regular feeding
is a problem*

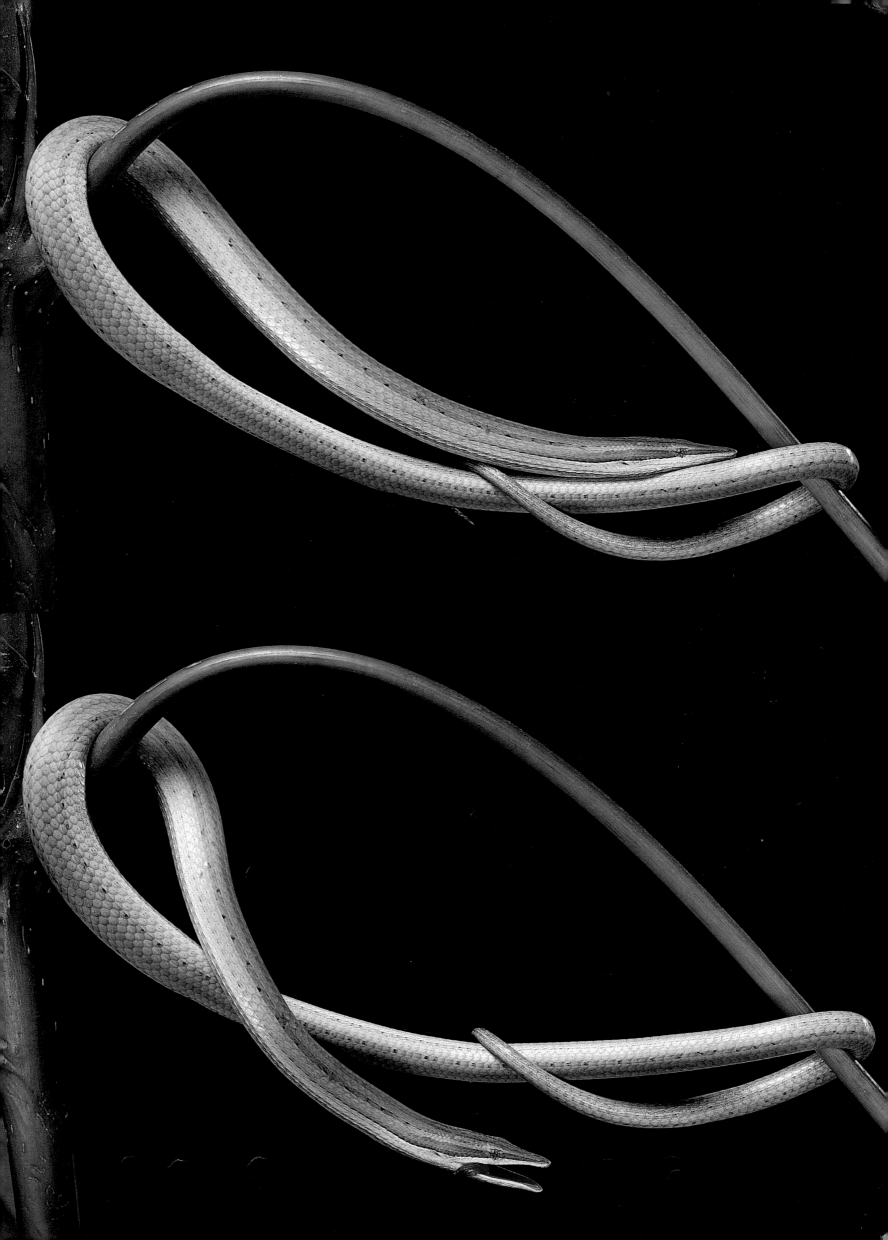

Scincoidae

This is the largest family of lizards, embracing a flourishing population of nearly 1,100 species distributed throughout the tropical regions of the world. Most are small, dull, shy creatures that hide from predators in nests on the ground. Others have evolved differently, such as the arboreal Solomon Islands Skink or the Australian Shingleback.

Skinks usually have smooth bodies with absurdly small legs that force them to move with an undulating motion like snakes.

The tail is often colored and used as a defense mechanism. When threatened, the skink deliberately sheds the tip of its tail that quivers and distracts the assailant's attention long enough for the skink to escape. Males and females look almost identical but may be distinguished by their distinctive pheromones. After a brief mating ceremony, the females either give birth to live young or lay eggs and in some cases will then guard them, displaying a maternal instinct rare in lizards.

This lizard is a model of parental care.
The female is ovoviparous and after 6-7 months gives birth to one or two babies that she looks after for several months. A prehensile tail and strong claws allow the skink to move easily among the trees of tropical forests. It is nocturnal and strictly vegetarian.

Corucia zebrata
[Solomon Islands Skink]

Distribution
Solomon Islands Archipelago (Micronesia, Western Pacific), the Buka Islands and Bougainville, Papua New Guinea

Average size
2–2ft. 7in.

Breeding details
A fascinating addition to any terrarium because of its unusual behavior. Endangered in the wild and worth breeding more often in captivity

This lizard has learned to make the most of humans
humans whose settlements provide it with hiding places and a plentiful supply of food. It is very adventurous when it comes to food and always prepared to taste our leftovers. For an inhabitant of a tropical forest faced with the increasing devastation of its natural habitat, it does seem to have adapted remarkably well.

Mabuya varia
Distribution
Great Lakes region of Africa

Average size
8in.

Following double-page illustration *Tribonolotus gracilis* [Crocodile Skink] **Details page 80**

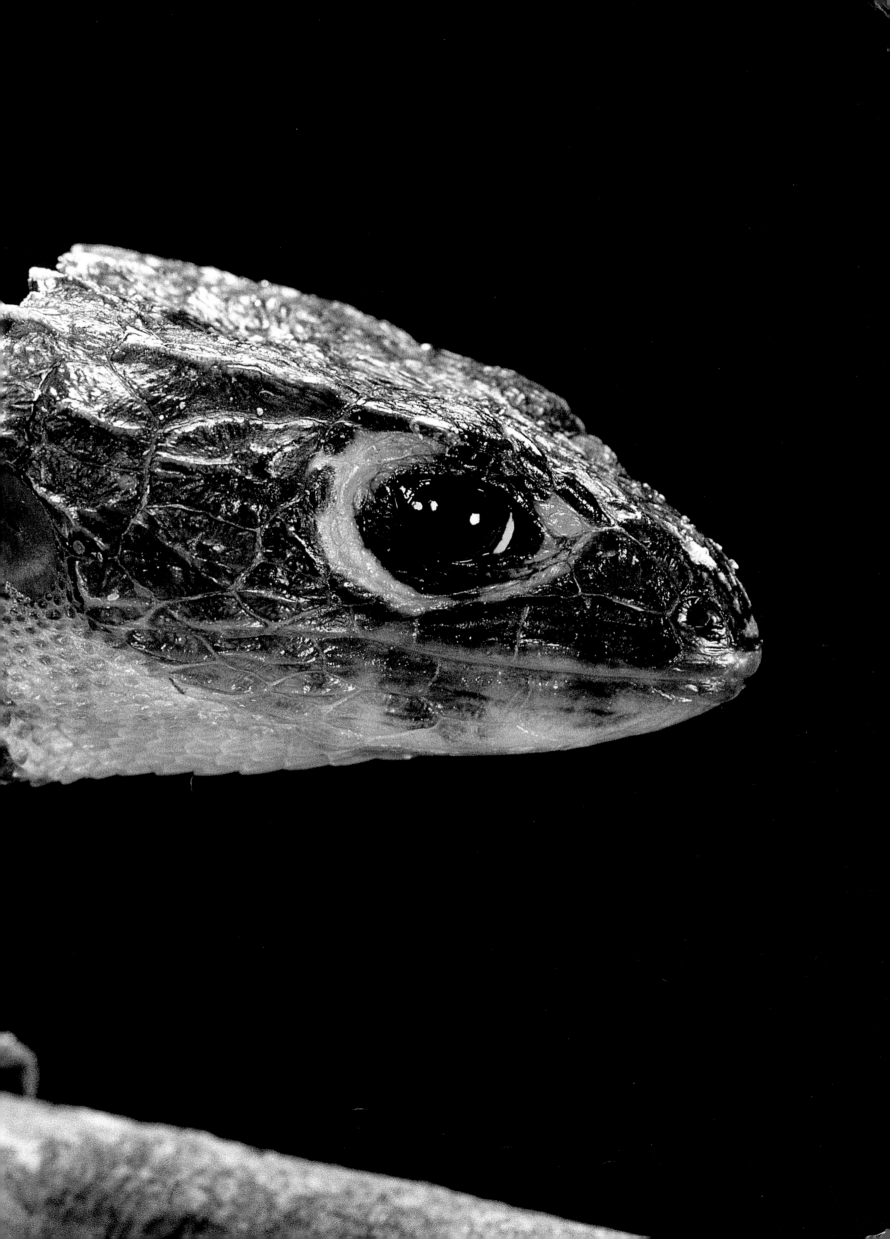

Teiidae
(Tegus and Whiptails)

Tegus are the American equivalent of the Varanidae (Monitor Lizards) found elsewhere. They comprise around 100 species found in a wide variety of ecological niches.

Tegus are large, powerful terrestrial predators with strong legs – the largest specimens may grow to 4.5ft in length. They are predominantly diurnal and oviparous but around a dozen species are parthenogenetic, which means that the females lay viable, unfertilized eggs requiring no fertilization by a male. There is even a bisexual species of tegu.

Rarely particular when it comes to food, certain aquatic species of tegu specialize in hunting snails that they crush between their flat, molar-like teeth.

Their size makes the tegus easy targets, hunted on a massive scale as much for their flesh as for their skin that makes excellent leather.

The largest lizard in South America after the Common Iguana, this sturdy, magnificent creature likes sunny grasslands within reach of humidity and rocky or forested areas. It is diurnal and spends most of its time hunting but also digs a burrow in which to sleep at night. The males are more active than the females, up earlier in the morning and later to retire at night. These lizards are quick to escape from predators, running on two legs if necessary, but if cornered they can be quite intimidating.

Tupinambis merianae
[Argentinian Black and White Tegu]

Distribution
Southern Argentina and Brazil, Paraguay and Uruguay

Average size
4ft.

Breeding details
The most docile and the most "intelligent" of the tegus and the easiest to breed and raise

This large lizard is reputed to be the most intelligent of all and its hunting tactics are certainly quite ingenious. It likes drier habitats than its cousin above [Tupinambis merianae] but otherwise their lifestyles are similar. Sadly tegu skin is much sought after by the leather industry but despite relentless hunting these lizards are still found in healthy numbers.

Tupinambis rufescens
[Red Tegu]

Distribution
Paraguay, Argentina

Average size
3ft

Breeding details
Good-natured and easily domesticated

Varanidae
(Monitor Lizards)

These are the largest of all the lizards and also among the most primitive. They include such famous giants as the Komodo Dragon that can grow to nearly 10ft in length but also much smaller "dragons" that are only a tenth of that size. There are some 40 species in the Varanidae family, all ferocious carnivores and insectivores distributed throughout the warm regions of Africa, Asia and especially Australia, which is home to more than two thirds of all known species.

Monitor lizards are predominantly diurnal and very active, always on the lookout for food that they find using their highly developed sense of smell. The forked tongue flicks out much like a snake's, to pick up "chemical cues" in the air that are then transferred for analysis to a special organ in the palate called Jacobson's Organ. Monitor Lizards are built for hunting, with sharp claws and powerful jaws. If cornered, they will lash the enemy with their tongue and strong, whip-like tail before biting and scratching if caught.

The Varanidae are oviparous, frequently laying their eggs in burrows to protect them from predators and keep them at a constant temperature.

Occasionally venturing into towns where it is a notorious scavenger, this monitor lizard feeds off almost anything, even carcasses, and no other species preys more successfully on eggs and baby crocodiles. It is aquatic by nature and may be found in any tropical habitat where it has access to water. It is formidably strong with a ferocious, lashing tail that makes it virtually impossible to approach.

Varanus niloticus
[Nile Monitor]

Distribution
Throughout Africa, south of the Sahara and Egypt

Average size
4.5ft

Breeding details
Unsuitable for rearing in captivity because of size and temperament

This lizard wraps its spiny tail around its body as protection from predators.
It is typically found in rocky habitats but also lives in tree trunks or wedges itself into burrows using its spiny appendage. Fairly tolerant of other lizards and rarely aggressive, it is among the smallest of the monitor lizards. It feeds off insects, lizards and tiny mammals.

Varanus acanthurus
[Spiny-tailed Monitor]

Distribution
Australia

Average size
19-20in.

Breeding details
Thanks to its good nature and reasonable size, this monitor lizard is one of those most frequently bred in captivity

Following double-page display *VVaranus doreanus* [Blue-tailed Monitor] **Details page 81**

● Agamidae

Acanthosaura armata
[Mountain Horn-headed Lizard]

Neither devil nor demon, this agamid is simply out to make an impression. The two pointed horns on the triangular-shaped head, the extremely scaly body and the spinal crest covered in sharp spikes are all contrivances to make it look ferocious. This semi-arboreal agamid lives in primary forest near water where it feeds off insects and, more surprisingly, earth worms.

Distribution
Thailand, Malaysia and Indonesia

Average size
10in.

● Agamidae

Hydrosaurus weberi
[Weber's Sail-fin Lizard]

This large aquatic dragon likes deep rivers in dense tropical forests. It is an excellent swimmer, gliding effortlessly through the water using the palmate webbing between its digits. One of its major features is the magnificent "sail-fin" on its tail. Adults are herbivores with a preference for brightly colored fruit.

Distribution
Indonesia

Average size
3–3ft. 7in.

Breeding details
*Timid and needs a
great deal of space*

● Agamidae

Leiolepis belliana
[Butterfly Agama]

This lizard forms relationships for life. It lives in small communities where it is predominantly monogamous – a feature rare enough to be worth mentioning. When threatened, it splays its brightly colored flanks to make its body look larger – which also helps it to absorb heat from the sun. It does well in hot climates where it lives in sandy habitats by the sea and along the coast.

Distribution
*South–East Asia from Myanmar
(formerly Burma) to Malaysia*

Average size
12–18in.

Breeding details
Hard to acclimatize

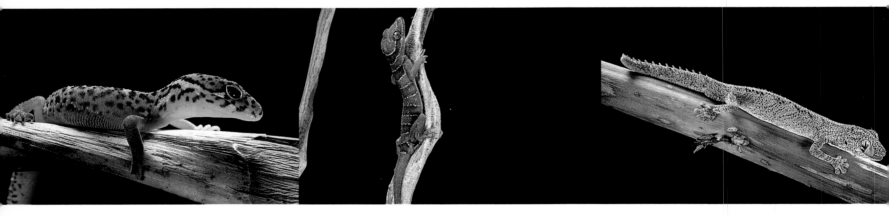

● Gekkonidae

Coleonyx mitratus
[Banded Gecko]

This small but intrepid character is unimpressed by larger assailants and when annoyed adopts an unusual pose and squeaks reproachfully through its half-open mouth. By day, this magnificent terrestrial gecko hides in burrows or crevices in tropical forests thinly scattered with trees. It is strictly insectivorous.

Distribution
Central America from Honduras to Panama

Average size
4in.

Breeding details
*A shy lizard although interesting
and frequently kept by beginners*

● Gekkonidae

Cyrtodactylus pulchellus
[Banded Forest Gecko]

This nocturnal lizard is equipped with large, clawed digits for climbing the 1,000 year-old trees and rocky cliffs of its chosen habitat. It lives in deep, dark, unspoiled rainforests at high altitude (up to 4,200 ft.) where it enjoys a steady supply of insects on which to prey.

Distribution
*Malaysia, Thailand, Myanmar
and northeast India*

Average size
8–9in.

Breeding details
Needs an environment with strong branches

● Gekkonidae

Diplodactylus ciliaris
[Spiny-tailed Gecko]

When threatened, this gecko contracts its muscles and ejects a repellent substance through the spines on its tail. The largest of its family, it is nocturnal and terrestrial and occurs in dry, low-lying vegetation. Its coloration is highly variable.

Distribution
Australia

Average size
7in.

Breeding details
*Any breeder lucky enough to
possess one of these is the envy
of reptile lovers*

Chamaeleonitidae
Chamaeleo calyptratus
[Veiled Dragon]

The largest chameleons in the world wear this huge, prominent veil to help disguise the shape of the head and camouflage them as they dart about in the undergrowth. It may also help the females of the species to recognize their male counterparts at first glance.

Distribution
Yemen and the borders
of Saudi Arabia

Average size
18in. (maximum 20-24in.)

Breeding details
Prolific, adaptable and the only chameleon frequently reared in captivity

Chamaeleonitidae
Chamaeleo dilepis
[Flap-necked Chameleon]

When threatened, this chameleon deploys a defense mechanism that remains hidden at other times: it unfurls hidden flaps in its skin to make itself look frightening - like an elephant flapping its ears. This is a very common lizard in East Africa where it lives in every kind of habitat - savanna, steppe, tropical and subtropical forests - and is especially fond of insects.

Distribution
Throughout East Africa and as far as South Africa

Average size
18in.

Breeding details
Too territorial and nervous to be kept in a terrarium

Chamaeleonitidae
Furcifer (Chamaeleo) oustaletti
[Oustalet's Chameleon]

This giant specimen has a voracious appetite and hunts anything it is capable of swallowing. It lives in the driest regions of the savanna and undoubtedly ranks as one of the largest chameleons in the world. Besides size, other distinctive features are a dull, grainy coat, small, streamlined veil and a very spiky dorsal crest. Like other chameleons, its size and color depend on geographic origin.

Distribution
Madagascar, introduced to Kenya

Average size
20in.

Breeding details
Calm inhabitant for vast terrarium

Gekkonidae
Eublepharis macularius/f. albinos/f. golden
[Leopard Gecko]

This brightly colored gecko spends the summer hunting - insects, spiders, centipedes, small lizards - and stores fat in its long tail for the winter fast. The Leopard Gecko has one of the longest life expectancies of all the lizards - the oldest recorded specimen lived for more than 30 years. Local people regard it as evil, no doubt because of its rather ghostly appearance.

Distribution
Pakistan, India, Afghanistan, Turkmenistan

Average size
8in.

Breeding details
Easily bred and reproduced on a grand scale — hence the mutated forms such as the "albino" and "golden" varieties much prized by collectors (page 52).

Gekkonidae
Phelsuma ornata
[Ornate Day Gecko]

See the description of the Day Gecko's on page 56.

Distribution
Mauritius

Average size
4-5in.

Breeding details
Likes a dry environment

Gekkonidae
Ptychozoon kuhli
[Flying Gecko]

This arboreal gecko takes to the air to escape predators. Using its palmate digits to control speed and direction, it glides effortlessly by means of the flaps of skin on its flanks and legs. Once safely landed in a tree, it camouflages itself to blend with the huge variety of moss and lichen that overlay the lush jungle where it lives.

Distribution
Burma, Thailand, Malaysia and Indonesia, the Nicobar and Andaman Islands (in the Indian Ocean)

Average size
8in.

Breeding details
Remarkably discreet

● Gekkonidae

Rhacodactylus ciliatus
[Eyelash Gecko]

This little known inhabitant of an isolated island is characterized by a stocky, streamlined body, and an astonishing triangular-shaped head with two rows of spike-like scales that start above the eyes and run back towards the shoulders – hence the name "Eyelash Gecko". It hunts by night amid the branches and feeds off insects and smaller lizards.

Distribution
New Caledonia, Isle of Pines

Average size
8in.

Breeding details
These lizards have been bred for no more than a decade or so but are already common in terrariums

● Gekkonidae

Uroplatus sikorae
[Mossy Leaf-tailed Gecko]

This gecko is entirely concealed by the lush mosses and lichens that grow on the trees of its native habitat. Disconcertingly motionless and invisible, it clings head-down to the tree trunk until nightfall when it emerges from its lethargy to go hunting insects until dawn. Seeing the bark come alive in this fashion is positively surreal...

Distribution
Madagascar

Average size
7in.

Breeding details
This magnificent specimen is the most sought-after gecko of the Uroplatus genus

● Iguanidae

Chalarodon madagascariensis

Iguanas being non-existent in the Old World, it is hard to explain how this species ever reached the islands of Madagascar, so far from its country of origin. It likes an open environment such as beaches or sand dunes with sparse vegetation where it is a fast runner despite the difficult terrain. It hunts by chasing its prey, laying down enough fat to see it through the short tropical winter when it digs itself into the sand.

Distribution
Madagascar

Average size
8in.

● Scincoidae

Lamprolepis (Dasia) smaragdina

This small lizard has a fine, conical head to help it forge a path through bark, crevices and holes. It is very active, arboreal and diurnal and lives in forests where it is constantly on the lookout for insects.

Distribution
Indonesia

Average size
8-9in.

● Scincoidae

Tiliqua (Trachydosaurus) rugosa
[Shingleback]

Shinglebacks, so-called because of their grainy scales, have disconcertingly truncated bodies and, like other members of the skink family, bright blue tongues that they display by gaping widely in the face of assailants. Often seen in couples in the mating season, Shinglebacks are fairly immobile and feed on whatever comes their way - young rodents, insects, birds, carrion and plants.

Distribution
South and southwest Australia

Average size
15-20in.

Breeding details
Very common in Australia and easily bred although rare in collections and extremely sought after

● Scincoidae

Tribonolotus gracilis
[Crocodile Skink]

This appealing little fellow lives in the debris of the virgin forests of Papua New Guinea. He is extremely shy in his natural habitat so it is a rare to catch a glimpse of that magnificent triangular-shaped head and bright eyes ringed with orange.

Distribution
Southern Papua New Guinea

Average size
6-8in.

● Iguanidae

Cyclura cornuta
[Rhinoceros Iguana]

This fugitive from prehistoric times, the inspiration for countless science fiction films and childish nightmares, is actually perfectly harmless. It likes a peaceful life and long sociable siestas in the sun interrupted only by violent battles between males. The tragic victim of its own appearance, it has been chased away from its native Caribbean beaches and dealt a death blow by the introduction of non-endemic creatures such as the mongoose that feasts off its eggs and young. Sadly, certain subspecies are already extinct.

Distribution
Dominican Republic, Haiti

Average size
4ft.

Breeding details
Rare, much sought after and the only terrestrial iguana that is often bred in captivity

● Iguanidae

Phrynosoma modestum
[Round-tail Horned Iguana]

With only its cryptic coloring to protect it, this iguana tends to lie buried in the sandy soil of the arid or semi-arid plains where it lives. It perfects its disguise by lying completely flat so as to avoid any telltale shadows - once buried it is indistinguishable from its surroundings. It is constantly on the lookout for food and eats mainly ants plus other tiny insects.

Distribution
Southern states of America and northern Mexico

Average size
1.5–3in.

Breeding details
Difficult to feed properly in captivity

● Iguanidae

Sceloporus cyanogenys
[Blue Spiny Lizard]

This giant among the Sceloporus is extremely fast and always braced to escape from snakes, its chief predators. It is diurnal and lives in colonies in arid, stony ground where it feeds off insects and smaller lizards. Males display more distinctive coloring in the reproductive period than females that remain much duller.

Distribution
Northern Mexico, Texas

Average size
12in.

Breeding details
Viviparous and often bred

● Varanidae

Varanus doreanus
[Blue-tailed Monitor]

This species was first described in 1874 then neglected for more than 100 years before being rediscovered in 1997. We know little about the habits of this shy creature that hides away in unspoiled, virgin forests, dashing for safety at the slightest noise. With a flash of its magnificent gradated blue tail, it vanishes into the depths of the tropical darkness. It is semi-arboreal and diurnal and a fairly opportunistic feeder.

Distribution
Papua New Guinea

Average size
4ft.

Breeding details
Fearful but not aggressive

● Varanidae

Varanus exanthematicus
[Savanna Monitor]

This shy lizard is always ready to plough the soil with its powerful claws in search of larvae – its favorite food. It is strictly seasonal in activity, spending six months of the year hiding in ground squirrels' burrows or termite hills and only emerging at the start of the rainy season. For the lizard, the rains bring a return to more clement weather and especially a rich supply of food: scarabs, millipedes and locusts.

Distribution
Distributed over a broad area from Senegal to Ethiopia

Average size
2ft. 7in.

Breeding details
The calmest of the monitor lizards and the most frequently found in terrariums

● Varanidae

Varanus rudicollis
[Black Rough-neck Monitor]

There is no shortage of myths about this enigmatic species that remains one of the most fascinating and little known of all the monitors – in Thailand for instance, it is widely believed to spit venom. It is so discreet that we cannot even be sure whether it is present in neighboring islands. The lizard's strangely bird-like head certainly helps to reach into narrow crevices in search of insects and larvae.

Distribution
Thailand, Myanmar, Malaysia, Sumatra and Borneo

Average size
4.5ft.

Breeding details
Impossible to tame and difficult to breed

Snakes

These unpopular creatures are the most misunderstood of all the reptiles. They comprise a family of 2,600 species that are distributed worldwide with the exception of the polar regions and areas at high altitude.

Snakes are also the longest reptiles having evolved directly from primitive lizards. This absence of legs though is not a defining feature since it is a characteristic they share with certain lizards. Serpentine locomotion is fast and undulating. Snakes have 200-400 vertebra that they use to propel themselves forward by pushing their body against rough ground or surface obstacles.

All snakes are virtually deaf due to the absence of any external ear opening (although they are capable of detecting vibration) and in place of eyelids, their eyes are protected by a transparent scale.

Snakes are strictly carnivorous but due to their low metabolic rate need surprisingly little food by our own mammalian standards. Certain species of large python survive on just two large kills a month; smaller species need a greater, more regular supply of food. The majority of snakes are capable of eating prey larger than their heads because their lower jawbones are only attached by an elastic ligament, allowing the lower part of the mouth to stretch remarkably.

Snakes capture their prey in two ways. Venomous snakes paralyze their prey by injecting it with venom. The victim eventually drops dead a few yards away and is eaten once the snake has recovered it. Non-venomous snakes bite, then wrap their prey in a crushing grip until it dies or has been swallowed. Some venomous species with poorly developed injection systems use a combination of both methods, biting the victim then retaining it without constriction until the venom does its work.

Female snakes are often bulkier and longer than males but otherwise have no visible distinguishing sexual characteristics. The only exception is the Madagascar Leaf-Nosed Snake (Langaha nasuta) that has a feeler-like appendage on the tip of its snout. In males this resembles a fine spike but in females it looks like a feather. Many oviparous species of snake seek out decomposing plants in which to lay their eggs (because of the heat and humidity produced). Some pythons "incubate" their eggs by contracting their muscles at regular intervals so as to raise the temperature of incubation by a few degrees. King Cobras actually stand guard over their nests. Viviparous or ovoviviparous species bring the eggs to term inside their bodies.

● **Previous double page** *Morelia viridis* [Green Tree Python] **Details page 145**
● **Left** *Python reticulatus* f. *tiger* [Reticulated Python] **Details page 98**

Boidae

This family of more than 84 species includes the real giants of the snake world – 19-23ft monsters with some as long as 30ft, although no larger so far as we know. Snakes of the Boidae family are regarded as primitive because they still retain vestigial legs.

Impressive though they surely are, large pythons and anacondas are not nearly as dangerous as they are made out to be. When cornered, they confront their assailant by hissing loudly before biting. The dreaded death by constriction is something they reserve for their prey – of which humans do not form part.

In addition to huge snakes the Boidae also includes many species of much smaller, more modest boas that are distributed worldwide, the smallest specimens measuring no more than 20in. Diet depends on size, but those that are large enough show a distinct preference for rodents.

Boas and anacondas are viviparous but pythons are oviparous, laying as many as 100 eggs at a time. The leather industry takes a heavy toll of the larger species while the smaller species suffer from the continuing destruction of their natural habitat.

This voracious hunter often devours snakes much larger than itself. Widespread throughout Papua New Guinea, the Papuan Python occurs in every kind of biotope although, sadly, it often finishes up under the wheels of a car.

Apodora papuana
[Papuan Python]

Distribution
*Papua New Guinea
and neighboring islands*
Average size
4.5-12ft. (the record stands at 16ft.)
Breeding details
No known specimens in captivity

When night falls, this expert hunter emerges from its hiding place to ambush mammals and birds amid the lush vegetation. It spends its day curled up on the ground or discreetly wrapped around a branch, away from prying eyes. The least widely distributed of the species, it likes waterside biotopes in dense tropical forests.

Morelia spilota cheynei
[Carpet Python]

Distribution
Northeast Queensland, Australia
Average size
5.5ft.
Breeding details
Shot to stardom in herpetological circles because of its striking coloring

The Carpet Python is so adaptable that it often encroaches on the biotopes of other snakes. Its preferred habitats are humid forests, rocky terrain, thorny grasslands and human settlements. The largest and the most widely distributed of its species, it is a voracious hunter that feeds off small mammals, lizards and birds.

Morelia spilota variegata
[Carpet Python]

Distribution
*Central Australia,
Papua New Guinea*
Average size
4.5–6.5ft.
Breeding details
*Docile and one of the
easiest pythons to
rear in captivity*

Like its cousin the Green Anaconda, the smaller but no less mythical Yellow Anaconda also spends most of its time in rivers, swamps and marshes (despite its arboreal habit) but more readily leaves the water to bask in the sun. It feeds predominantly off mammals, birds, fish and any reptiles it is capable of swallowing.

Eunectes notaeus
[Yellow Anaconda]

Distribution
*Bolivia to southwest Brazil,
Paraguay, Uruguay and
northwest Argentina*
Average size
6.5–10ft.
Breeding details
*Easy to rear but
often temperamental*

This Burrowing
Python uses the
same defense tactic
as its close relative
the Ball Python:
it rolls into a ball around its head
leaving its truncated, head-shaped
tail exposed to discourage would-
be predators. The only genuinely
fossorial python, it is too small to
eat anything larger than rodents
and lizards.

Calabaria reinhardtii

Distribution
West and Central Africa

Average size
2ft. 7in.- 3ft. 7in.

This snake
undergoes a rare
color transformation:
the bright orange and black colors
that protect vulnerable juveniles
from predators turn darker in
adulthood to improve camouflage.
The Bothrochilus Boa is found
exclusively in the Bismarck
Archipelago off northeastern
Papua New Guinea.

*Bothrochilus Boa
(previously Liasis Boa)*

Distribution
Bismarck Archipelago

Average size
3.6- 5.5ft.

Breeding details
*The only problem
is finding breeders*

This slender giant is often overlooked by lists of the world's largest snakes despite one Australian specimen, recorded in 1948, measuring 28ft. The Amethistina Python is found in a wide variety of habitats – from savanna to tropical forests – up to altitudes of 5,000 ft.

Morelia amethistina
[Amethistina Python]

Distribution
*Northeast coast of Australia,
Papua New Guinea
and neighboring islands*

Average size
10-13ft.

Breeding details
*Easy to rear but
beware its
temperamental nature*

The skin of the appropriately named "Diamond Python" glitters in the sun like a multifaceted gemstone. This masterpiece of nature lives in extreme climates where the temperature can drop to freezing in winter, driving our fascinating friend to hibernate in hencoops, under the eaves of roofs and in garages – much to the surprise of the owners.

Morelia spilota spilota
[Diamond Python]

Distribution
East coast of New South Wales

Average size
5-6ft.

Breeding details
*Much sought after for
its beauty but difficult
to breed in captivity*

This shimmering rainbow of mother-of-pearl spends most of its time hiding from prying eyes. The White-lipped Python is an extremely shy snake that likes waterside habitats where there is an abundant supply of prey. Depending on geographic origin, it may be gold, dark amber or brown with the back darker than the sides.

Leiopython albertisii
[White-lipped Python]

Distribution
*Papua New Guinea
and satellite islands*

Average size
3–6ft. (maximum 10ft.)

Breeding details
*Easy to rear despite a shy,
nervous disposition*

Python or snake?

After years of doubt, scientists have confirmed that this enigmatic species is closer to snakes than pythons. It is fossorial and lives in the rain forests of Central America.

Loxocemus bicolor
[New World Sunbeam Snake]

Distribution
*Southern Mexico
to Costa Rica*

Average size
*2ft. 7in.
(maximum 4ft.)*

The ghostly Black Python haunts the highland rain forests of Papua New Guinea, a rare and unforgettable sight as it slithers through dark, hilly vegetation overgrown with mosses and lichen. In the dim light that filters through the forest canopy, this fascinating snake shimmers in iridescent shades of deepest blue.

Morelia boeleni
[Black Python, Boelen's Python]

Distribution
*The highlands of
Papua New Guinea*

Average size
6–8ft.

Breeding details
Extremely rare in captivity

The Reticulated Python, the largest snake in the world

and the longest of the Boidae, can measure up to 29ft. Although less massive than anacondas, adult "Retics" (as they are known) grow to a weight and mass that limit their arboreal lifestyle, although they remain excellent swimmers and have colonized countless islands. Diet is highly eclectic ranging from young cervids to any household pets they find on their territory. A range of magnificent color variations have been achieved in captivity by genetic selection, a technique that is increasingly used by breeders to produce such splendid specimens as the "Tiger Python" shown on page 84.

Python reticulatus
[Reticulated Python]

This famous leopard skin is worn by the Ball Python, the most

representative and popularized of all the pythons, worshipped by certain animist ethnic groups in Benin who include it in their religious ceremonies. The name "Ball Python" refers to its peculiar habit of curling into a ball around its head to protect itself.

Python regius
[Ball Python]

Distribution
Western Senegal to Nigeria and parts of Central Africa
Average size
3–4ft. (maximum 6ft.)
Breeding details
Widely bred in captivity although clutches are small

There are less than 20 known specimens of this extremely rare, mutated "Calico" python that is only found in

the wild. Although the exact process remains a mystery to collectors, loss of pigmentation is thought to be genetic, developing as the snake matures.

Python reticulatus **f.** *calico*
[Calico Python]

Distribution
Throughout South East Asia, Malaysia, Borneo, Java, Sumatra, Timor, Ceram and the Philippines
Average size
13–20ft. (maximum 29.5 ft.)
Breeding details
A fascinating colossus to rear in captivity but treat with respect — it needs careful handling

Following double-page display *Boa constrictor constrictor* [Boa Constrictor] **Details page 102** ●

Mouth gaping and hissing loudly the
Argentine Boa goes into defense
mode – but its theatrical
performance is all for show.
In the course of evolution, this
southernmost subspecies of
boa has adapted to a widely
fluctuating range of temperatures
and developed a very dark skin
capable of absorbing heat
from the sun more efficiently.

Boa constrictor occidentalis
[Argentine Boa Constrictor]

Distribution
*Northern Argentina,
southeast Bolivia and
parts of Paraguay*
Average size
Nearly 3ft.
Breeding details
*Strictly protected
in the wild by the
Washington Convention
but occasionally kept
by specialized breeders*

○ Previous double-page display

When threatened by a predator like man, this so-called "killer" snake actually prefers to avoid
confrontation, never attacking man
without reason. If cornered
however, it hisses fiercely at the
intruder with its mouth wide open.
Terrestrial and semi-arboreal, it
hunts by night – small mammals,
birds, lizards – ambushing its prey
and then squeezing it to death in
its vice-like grip.

Boa constrictor constrictor
[Boa Constrictor]

Distribution
*Amazonian forests
of Colombia to
northern Argentina*
Average size
6.5-10ft. (up to 15ft.)
Breeding details
*Frequently bred
in captivity for its
docile nature and
spectacular coloring*

This highly unusual, arboreal boa is characterized by a fierce-looking, very prominent head,
exaggerated lips, short, prehensile
tail and cryptic coloring. It remains
hidden in the trees by day,
only descending at night to
ambush small mammals,
birds and other prey.

Sanzinia madagascariensis
[Madagascar Tree Boa]

Distribution
East coast of Madagascar
Average size
5-7ft.
Breeding details
*Frequently bred
in captivity for its
docile nature and
spectacular coloring*

Colubridae

This immense, cosmopolitan family of 1,700 species, found in every kind of biotope except for the very coldest, is by far the most common group of snakes, including a great many relatively unknown species. Often slender with cryptic coloring, colubrids are expert hunters and highly efficient at controlling vermin in rural areas

Their diet is very varied: insects, spiders, mollusks, other snakes, birds, eggs, rodents and even lobsters.

Some rear-fanged colubrids do produce venom but the vast majority are harmless to humans. Sadly, however, they are regularly confused with venomous species and destroyed through sheer ignorance. They are also preyed on by large numbers of birds and considered a delicacy by other reptiles.

Terrestrial colubrids are oviparous but aquatic varieties are viviparous.

Due to the shape of its head, this is the only snake to possess frontal binocular vision: a significant advantage when hunting the lizards and amphibians that make up the bulk of its diet. To improve its camouflage, the Oriental Whip Snake moves in an irregular fashion, mimicking a branch swaying lightly in the wind. This is a venomous colubrid but the venom produced (from small, rear fangs) is purely digestive in function.

Ahaetulla prasina
[Oriental Whip Snake]

Distribution
*India to Indonesia
and the Philippines*

Average size
4–5ft.

Breeding details
*Frequently bred in captivity
for its docile nature and
spectacular coloring*

Without a doubt the most beautiful snake in Pakistan

the Diadem Snake matures from a dull colored juvenile into a magnificent orange-red adult with asymmetrical black markings. It lives in savanna and rocky steppes where the temperature fluctuates widely between day and night and the winters are harsh, forcing the Diadem to hibernate for several months. Diet is very varied and includes lizards, rodents and even ground-nesting birds.

Spalerophis diadema attriceps
[python tapis]

Distribution
North Africa, Middle and Near East, India and Pakistan

Average size
4 ft.

Breeding details
An active species that is increasingly bred in captivity

The trowel-shaped snout serves to dig out toads

– the favorite prey of this short, stocky snake that not only looks uncannily like an adder but also inflates its body like one to defend itself. When all else fails, it resorts to a defense tactic of its own: playing dead, motionless on its back with its mouth wide open.

Heterodon nasicus
[Western Hognose Snake]

Distribution
USA

Average size
2 ft. 7 in.

Breeding details
Only captive-bred specimens do well in captivity

To look intimidating,
this snake gapes widely
revealing the interior of its blue-black
mouth. Semi-arboreal and diurnal, it
spends its days in trees and bushes
by the water, feeding off amphibians.
Its favorite habitats are wet savanna
lands on high plateaus or
mountainous forests.

Philothamnus angolensis
[Angola Green Snake]

Distribution
*Many scattered groups
from Cameroon to Botswana*

Average size
2ft. 4in. — 3ft.

Breeding details
Difficult to feed

All the fires of creation
pale into insignificance
beside this splendidly
iridescent, sinuous
snake. Breathtakingly beautiful, it
is also an expert hunter of the lizards
and amphibians that share its habitat
amid the rain forests.

Drymobius margaritiferus
[Speckled Racer]

Distribution
*Central America from
southern Texas to Colombia*

Average size
1–4ft.

Breeding details
*An active species that
is increasingly bred
in captivity*

At the first sign of
trouble, this snake
lashes the air wildly
with its electric blue
tongue meanwhile folding up
like a concertina and inflating its
tracheal air sac – a defensive
performance guaranteed to
disconcert any intruder. The
coloration of this long arboreal
colubrid varies widely depending
on geographic origin. It lives in all
sorts of habitats, even venturing
into mangrove swamps.

Gonyosoma oxycep
[Red-tail Ratsnake]

Distribution
Throughout southeastern Asia

Average size
5ft. 3in.

Breeding details
*Difficult to acclimatize;
wild specimens are
often a problem
in terrariums*

Following double-page display *Elaphe guttata guttata* [Cornsnake] **Details page 144**

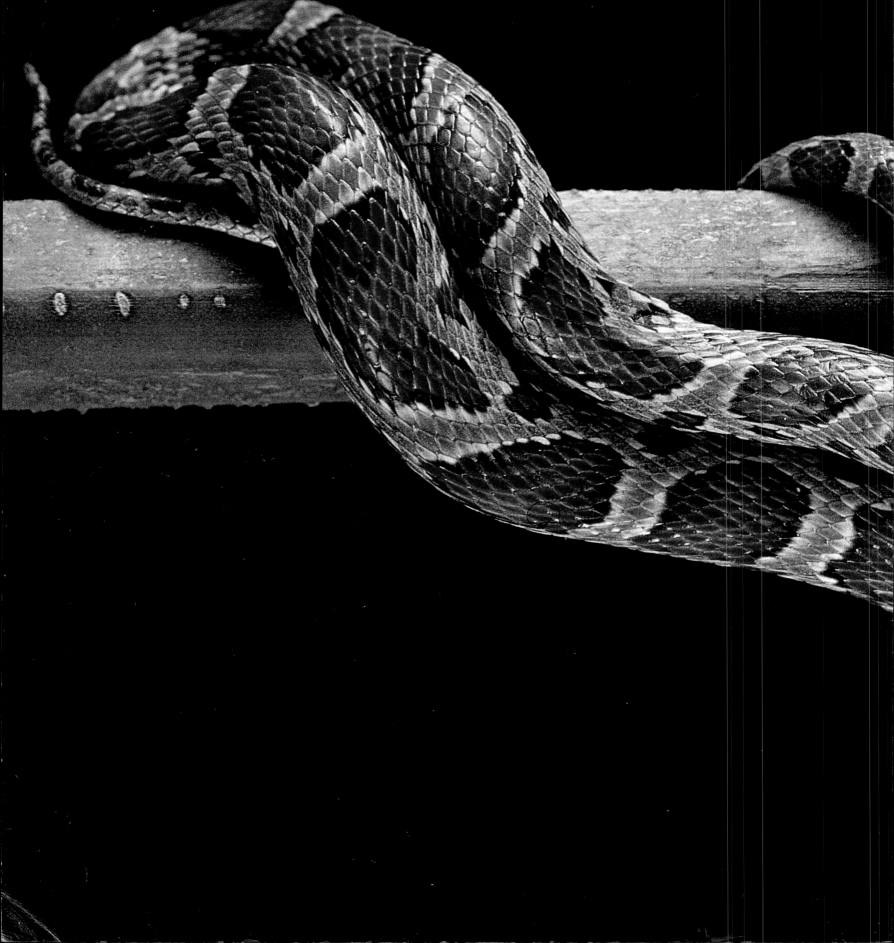

Although smaller, this European Leopard Snake has no reason to be envious of its more exotic American relative, the Cornsnake – with which it plainly has much in common in terms of color and pattern. It prefers fairly dry regions where it basks in the sun before setting off to hunt rodents and birds, often raiding their nests.

Elaphe situla
[Leopard Snake]

Distribution
*Greece, southern Italy,
Albania, Bulgaria,
Yugoslavia, Turkey*

Average size
2ft. 3in. – 3ft.

Breeding details
*Not widely available
and therefore fairly
rare in captivity*

Known as the "Beauty Snake" throughout South East Asia, this species is universally renowned for its markings. Its immense area of distribution includes temperate and tropical zones and a variety of habitats up to 10,000 ft: wasteland, rice paddies, caves and often under the eaves of roofs. It eats virtually anything but is especially fond of raiding nests for baby birds and rodents.

Elaphe taeniura friesi
[Beauty Snake]

Distribution
*China to Manchuria and
also the island of Taiwan
in the case of the subspecies
Elaphe taeniura friesi*

Average size
6–7ft. (maximum 9ft.)

Breeding details
*Docile and fascinating
despite its size*

This snake is named after the river Amur that runs through its habitat on the boundary between China and Russia. It has developed a high metabolic rate to survive in the harsh climate and can digest food in the record time of 24 hours. Adults have magnificent black and yellow markings; juveniles are darker.

Elaphe schrencki schrencki
[Russian Amur Ratsnake]

Distribution
*The boundary between
Mongolia, China and Russia*

Average size
4–5ft. 3in.

Breeding details
*Easy-going and prolific
— a good candidate
for captive breeding*

In America, this species is also known as "Lampropeltis Variable" because none of the hatchlings in a clutch look alike

– there is no standard color or pattern. It likes dry, warm habitats where it feeds on lizards, rodents and occasionally other snakes.

Lampropeltis mexicana mexicana
[Mexican Kingsnake]

Distribution
Mexico

Average size
3–3.5ft.

Breeding details
Often confused with its cousin, Lampropeltis alterna [Gray–Banded Kingsnake]

By mimicking the venomous "Coral Snake" this harmless Honduran Milk Snake makes sure that it is left in peace – only an expert could tell the difference. This striped, colorful character slithering across the green forest floor is an incongruous sight. It looks totally out of place in a tropical forest where its rather garish coloring clashes with the natural tones of the animals and plants around it.

Lampropeltis triangulum hondurensis
[Honduran Milk Snake]

Distribution
Honduras, Nicaragua

Average size
4.5ft.

Breeding details
One of the most sought after and popular of the "fake corals"

Following double-page display *Boiga dendrophila melanota* [Mangrove snake] **Details page 118**

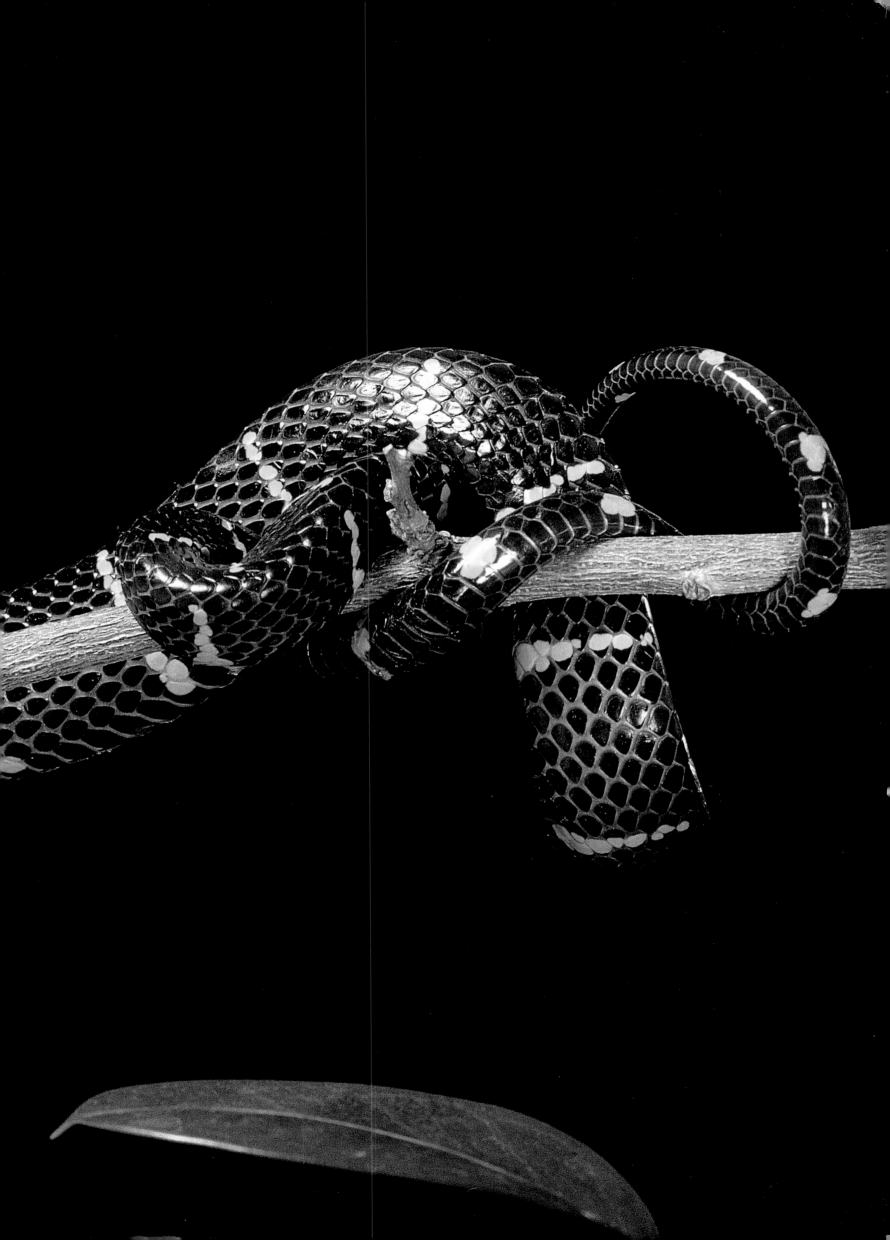

Previous double-page display ●

Those small rear fangs could be dangerous....

They belong to a lowland jungle snake found mainly in mangrove swamps that hunts by night in the branches overhanging the water. Its markings – suspiciously like those of the dangerous Bungarus faciatus – are a mimetic device to discourage predators. It feeds off birds and small mammals.

Boiga dendrophila melanota
[Mangrove Snake]

Distribution
*Southern Thailand,
Malaysia, Singapore,
Indonesia, Philippines*

Average size
5–7ft.

Breeding details
*Not suitable for rearing
in captivity because
its venom is too virulent*

Despite its uncanny resemblance to the Black Mamba this sleek,

arboreal snake is not venomous – although it does put on a convincingly terrifying performance, inflating its tracheal air sac to puff out its enormous scales. Thanks to its ability to move very quickly when hunting, it feeds off a wide selection of prey.

Thrasops jacksoni
[Jackson's Tree Snake]

Distribution
*Great Lakes region,
Uganda, Tanzania,
Kenya, Democratic
Republic of the Congo,
Burundi and Rwanda*

Average size
5.5ft.

Breeding details
*Only recently became
available but already
popular in terrariums*

This small nocturnal and arboreal

snake is an expert snail catcher, prizing the hapless mollusks out of their shells with great dexterity. It has a very distinctive appearance - rectangular head, huge eyes, compact, very elongated, lichen-colored body - and lives in tropical virgin forests.

Aplopeltura boa
[Blunt-headed Tree Snake]

Distribution
*Southern Thailand,
Malaysia, Borneo,
Sumatra, Java, Philippines*

Average size
23.5in

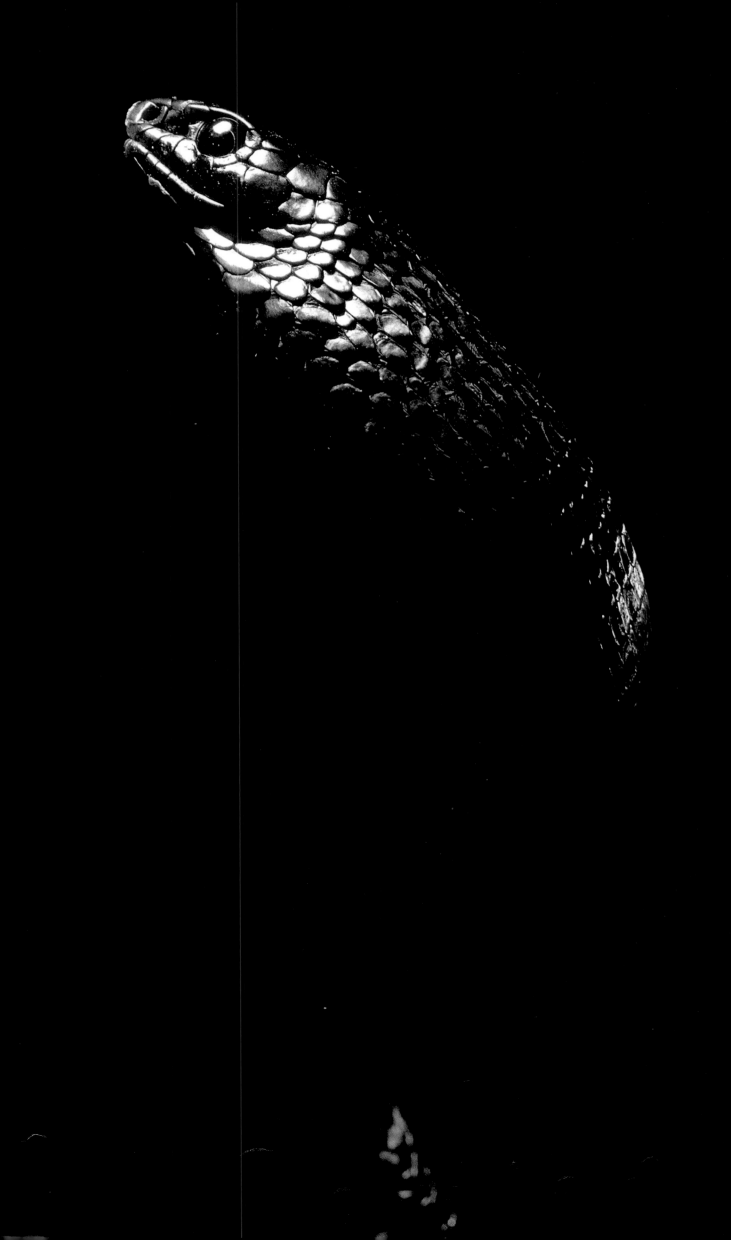

Elapidae

All elapids are venomous so, although they may look the same as grass snakes at first glance, the sooner you learn to tell the difference the better. Cobras, mambas, coral snakes, tiger snakes – these are some of the deadliest snakes in the world, with short, fixed, single groove fangs at the front of the upper jaw and venom so virulent that one bite can prove fatal.

Among this impressive family of 280 species we find the largest venomous snake in the world – the King Cobra measuring up to 16ft – and the most toxic – in Australia, for instance. The Elapidae also includes some 70 species of exclusively aquatic sea snakes that, although docile in nature, produce some of the most toxic venom known to man. The majority of elapids however are nothing like as forbidding, being on the contrary, small, discreet, even inoffensive creatures that rarely come into contact with man.

All the elapids move very fast when hunting prey – mammals, birds and especially reptiles – that they locate using their highly developed sense of smell.

They live in tropical and subtropical regions where they have adapted to a wide variety of ecological niches including that cradle of evolution, the sea.

The Egyptian Cobra, symbol of the Egyptian dynasties

and widely used as a decorative motif in temples, remains as famous as ever throughout Africa. If disturbed by day, this nocturnal, crepuscular creature vents its fury by rearing up and spreading the skin of its neck to form a hood, meanwhile swaying lightly from side to side as it follows the intruder's movements. One bite of its highly neurotoxic venom will rapidly paralyze the muscles of the respiratory system.

Naja Haje
[Egyptian Cobra]

Distribution
Throughout the African continent, as far as the Arabian Peninsula

Average size
5ft.

This cobra is believed
to possess
aphrodisiac powers
and is eaten by local men to
promote strength and virility. The
Monocled Cobra – so-called because
of the monocle mark at the rear of
the hood – has a much wider hood
than its African relatives and when
erect conveys an impression of
power and nobility that has seduced
countless illustrators. Although its
reputation for aggression is justified,
it never attacks gratuitously and only
bites when cornered or accidentally
stepped on.

Naja kaouthia
[Monocled Cobra]

Distribution
*India to southwest
China, South–East Asia
and as far as the
Malaysian Peninsular*
Average size
4ft.

At rest, this brightly
colored little snake could
easily be taken for a grass
snake but when alarmed, it quickly
rears up to reveal its true identity. If
that does not serve to deter intruders,
it then contracts its muscles while
simultaneously exhaling strongly so as to
fire two streams of venom from its fangs,
aiming with remarkable accuracy for a
reflective surface such as the victim's
eyes. Although the objective is to cause
temporary blindness, the damage
caused is often permanent. This cobra's
venom is such a lethal cocktail that one
bite almost invariably leads to death if
untreated.

Naja pallida
[Red Spitting Cobra]

Distribution
East Africa to Uganda
Average size
3ft.

Following double-page display *Dendroaspis angusticeps* [Green Mamba] **Details page 147**

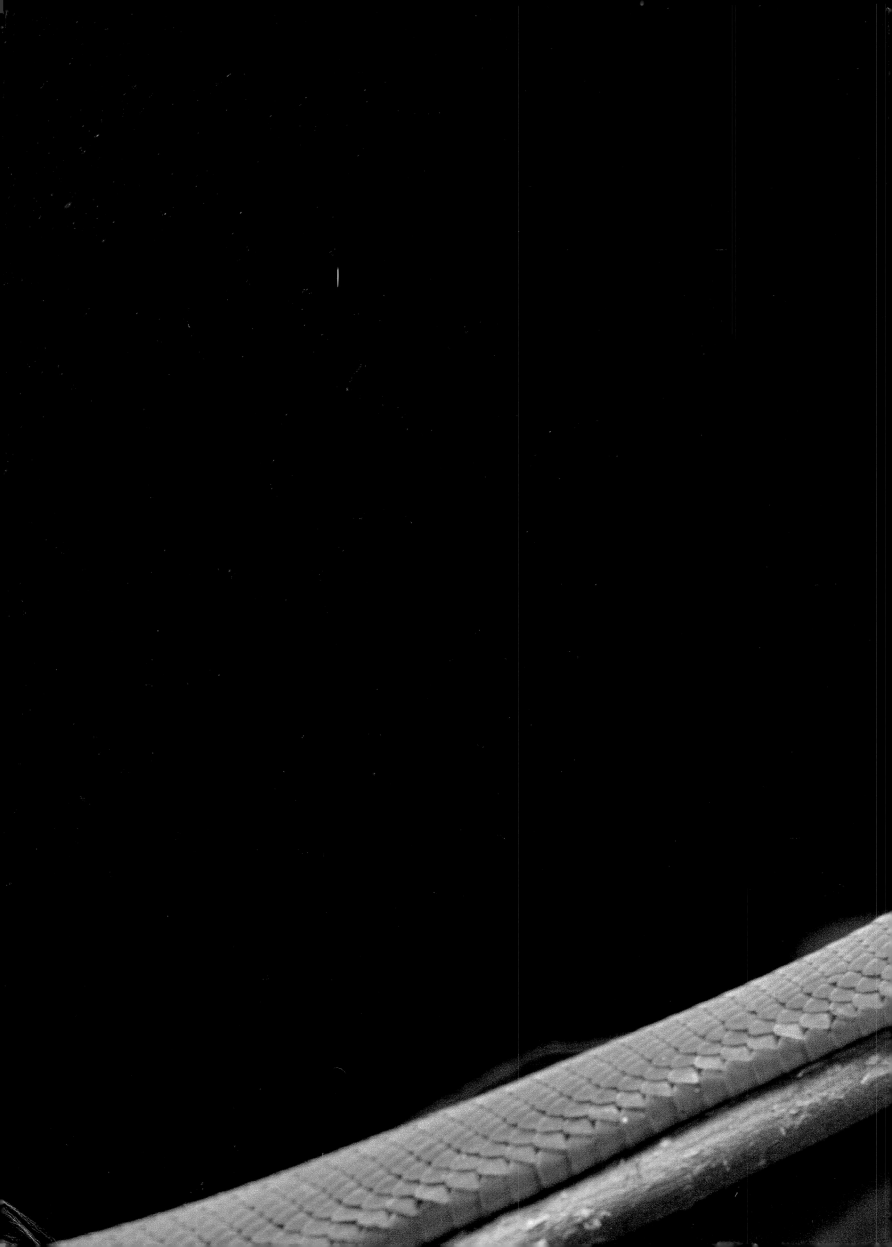

Viperidae
(vipers and adders)
and Crotalidae
(rattlesnakes or pit vipers)

These two families that include 150 known species of rattlesnake and 43 species of viper are often regarded as the most advanced of the snakes because of their uniquely efficient envenomating apparatus. Vipers and rattlesnakes have large, curved, folding fangs that spring forward when the mouth is open, injecting venom under pressure like a syringe. These snakes strike at lightning speed, often before the victim even realizes what is happening.

Both families have cryptic coloring and mainly hunt by positioning themselves at points regularly used by their prey and lying in wait – sometimes for weeks at a time. Once bitten, the victim is immediately released and crawls off to die some distance away. The snake can easily find it again later using its highly developed sense of smell.

One of the characteristics of the Crotalus – that they share with the Boidae – is a heat sensitive organ between the eye and the nostril that can detect temperature differences to a thousandth of a degree. Called the pit organ, it projects information into the snake's field of vision creating a stereoscopic image that allows the snake to track and strike with extraordinary accuracy.

This beautiful viper is one of the most dangerous snakes in Europe but luckily, being timid by nature, it prefers flight to fight and fatal encounters are rare. It likes a dry, sunny habitat in rocky scrub vegetation where it hunts by day or night depending on the season.

Vipera ammodytes
[Long-nosed Viper]

Distribution
Southeast Europe, northeast Italy and as far as the Lebanon

Average size
2ft. 7in.

Following double-page display *Bitis gabonica* [East African Gaboon Viper] **Details page 130**

Before it attacks, this little viper makes a distinctive hissing sound by rubbing together the saw-toothed scales of its coils. It lives in dry West African savanna but tends to gravitate towards human settlements in search of rodents and lizards. This increases the risk of a fatal encounter with a snake that already kills thousands of people each year with its virulently cytotoxic and hemorrhagic venom. The Echis species is regarded as one of the deadliest in the world.

Echis leucogaster
[White-bellied Carpet Viper]

Distribution
Mauritania to Chad

Average size
19–20in.

○ Previous double-page display

Two-inch long fangs (a world record) and large-capacity venom glands enable this snake to inject so much venom that the chances of survival are virtually nil. Impressively large and one of the heaviest of the venomous snakes it has a very wide head (6 in across) and strikes with lightning speed despite its apparent lethargy. Its effectively leafy coloration and ability to remain perfectly still, render it practically invisible amid the debris of the rain forests.

Bitis gabonica
[Gaboon Viper]

Distribution
Guinea to Angola, throughout central Africa and from Kenya to Zambia

Average size
1,20 m
4ft. (maximum 6ft.)

This viper accounts for a large proportion of the venomous snakebites in Africa including some that are fatal. It injects a large quantity of venom deep into its victim causing massive tissue death and permanent, irreversible damage. By day, this large and irascible viper relies on its cryptic coloration for camouflage but if disturbed it folds up like a concertina, inflating its body and hissing loudly to vent its fury.

Bitis arietans
[Puff Adder]

Distribution
The Sahara to South Africa

Average size
3ft.

This shy, timid species produces highly virulent venom but rarely bites.

By day, it rests in crevices and cracks among the rocks or under stones, emerging at nightfall to hunt small mammals, lizards and birds. It likes steep, sunny hills carpeted with rocky, scrub and may be found up to altitudes of more than 6,500 ft.

Daboia lebetina mauritanica

Distribution
Morocco, Algeria, Tunisia, western Libya
Average size
4ft.

Fatal encounters with this highly dangerous species have risen considerably in recent years due to mounting human encroachment on its territory. The people concerned are taking a serious risk: this viper's bite is fatal in 90 percent of untreated cases and 70 percent of treated cases.

Echis ocellatus
[West African Carpet Viper]

Distribution
Senegal to West Central Africa
Average size
16in.

Following double-page display *Atheris chloroechis* [West African Bush Viper] **Details page 146**

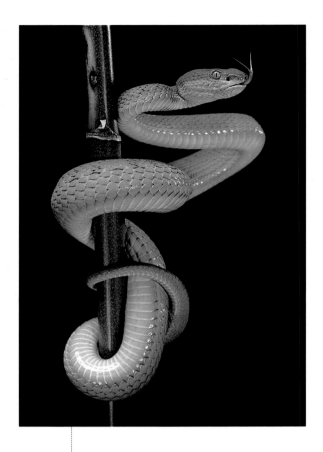

This pit viper is frequently kept as a talisman in "snake temples" where it is handled by priests who are either very brave or very foolish for despite its reputation for docility, it is in fact highly dangerous to humans. Often found lurking near houses, it accounts for a large number of snakebites in South East Asia. Strictly arboreal and nocturnal, it is as common in tropical virgin forests as in plantations.

Trimeresurus albolabris
[White-lipped Pit Viper]

Distribution
Throughout South-East Asia from India to China and Indonesia

Average size
2ft. 3 in.

When faced with an intruder, this rattlesnake is very unpredictable: it might commence rattling or remain completely still. But beware – it is highly dangerous and strikes before you know it. The color and pattern of the Tiger Rattlesnake vary greatly from population to population. It is exclusively found in canyons, ravines and other steep, dry places where it feeds mainly on lizards and a few rodents. It is diurnal early in the season becoming progressively more nocturnal as daytime temperature rises.

Crotalus tigris
[Tiger Rattlesnake]

Distribution
Southern Arizona to northern Mexico

Average size
2ft. 3in.

The essence of Mayan belief in the eternal cycle of birth and rebirth was inspired by the shedding of this snake's skin. Worshipped by many of Central America's Amerindian tribes, this species guarded sacred places against evil spirits and was a feature of serpent iconography. It likes tropical wooded savanna lands where it leads a very discrete existence, preferring to escape rather than use its tiny rattle. When it does bite, it injects a large quantity of virulent venom.

Crotalus durissus durissus
[Cascabel]

Distribution
The "durissus" subspecies occurs across large parts of South America and as far as Central America
Average size
4ft.

Like all rattlesnakes, this ferocious predator has a heat- sensitive "pit organ" that helps it to strike accurately even in total darkness. Its invariably dark-colored tail ends in a small rattle (rarely used despite its bad temper) that grows by another segment each time it sheds its skin. The Cascabel hunts by night in the dry grasslands where it lives, ambushing small rodents and lizards.

Crotalus durissus terrificus
[Cascabel]

Distribution
Bolivia, Paraguay, Uruguay and southern Brazil
Average size
4ft.

Forever associated with the dusty plains of the Wild West, this rattlesnake is one of the largest in the USA. Despite its girth and death-dealing powers, it asks only to be left in peace and hates being disturbed. When annoyed, it vibrates the rattle in its tail, something that is thought to have evolved as a defense against being trampled by the large herds of bison that roamed the prairies. Sadly, Diamondbacks are slaughtered wholesale each year in popular "rattlesnake roundups" when their flesh is eaten for effect and their heads are chopped off and made into belt buckles and other tasteless trophies.

Crotalus atrox
[Western Diamondback Rattlesnake]

Distribution
Southern and southwestern states of America
Average size
*1,50 m
5ft. (maximum 8ft.)*

The Prairie
Rattlesnake covers
a huge territory,
occupying many
different biotopes
ranging from wet and dry prairies
to forest boundaries, the edges of
deserts and mountainous terrain.
Its venom is highly virulent, and
although not necessarily fatal, has
serious physical consequences.

Crotalus viridis
[Prairie Rattlesnake]

Distribution
*Western states of America
to southern British
Columbia and Canada*

Average size
4ft.

This very discreet
inhabitant of the
sweeping Venezuelan
grasslands basks for
only a short time in the
sun before retreating to hide in the tall,
tangled grasses. It hunts by night –
small mammals, lizards and
occasionally birds – and, although
extremely dangerous, has little or no
opportunity to bite humans owing
to its remote habitat away from man.

Crotalus vegrandis
[Urocoan Rattlesnake]

Distribution
Venezuela

Average size
2ft. 5in.

Following double-page display *Agkistrodon contortrix* [Southern Copperhead] **Details page 147**

● Boidae

Acrantophis madagascariensis
[Madagascan Ground Boa]

Unlike its prolific South American
relative, the boa constrictor, the
Madagascan Ground Boa's
reproductive strategy is to produce a
few very large hatchlings (25in) that are
better able to defend themselves
against predators. Mainly terrestrial, it
lives in the Madagascan wetlands
where it feeds off small lemurines,
rodents and lizards.

Distribution
North Madagascar

Average size
Up to 6ft.

Breeding details
*Since captive breeding was authorized in 1997,
this snake has become a popular addition to
European terrariums*

● Boidae

Candoia carinata carinata
[Solomon Islands Boa]

This totally inoffensive little boa seems
to have a talent for mimicry. Not only
does it look uncannily like the Death
Adder (Acantophis sp.) but it also
apparently uses its tail (which is much
lighter than its body) as bait to catch
unsuspecting amphibians and lizards.
Little more is known about this boa
that is rarely observed in the wild.

Distribution
Indonesia, Papua New Guinea, Solomon Islands

Average size
1.5-3ft.

● Boidae

Lichanura trivirgata trivirgata
[Rosy Boa]

One of the rare species of American
boa, this fairly docile character lives in
rocky deserts where prey is scarce. To
make up for the absence of food, it is
able to store fat faster than other
snakes – often becoming obese in
captivity owing to food that is too rich
or too plentiful.

Distribution
*Southern California, west and south Arizona and
northern Mexico*

Average size
2ft. 3in.

● Boidae

Python timoriensis
[Lesser Sundas Python]

This rare and little known species that
is not found on the island of Timor
despite its Latin nomenclature, is one
of the most beautiful with its highly
iridescent olive to straw-yellow skin
and dark brown markings. Also very
striking is the massive head that is
conspicuous on such a slender body.

Distribution
The Island of Flores, in Indonesia

Average size
6ft.

Breeding details
Slow to reach sexual maturity

● Colubridae

Dasypeltis scabra
[Egg-eating Snake]

This snake, capable of swallowing an
egg although not much bigger than a
finger, is an expert tree-climber with a
talent for discovering and raiding nests.
It is entirely harmless but puts on a
bold show of aggression for intruders:
coiling up to attack, it gapes widely and
makes a rattling sound by rubbing
together the scales of its coils.

Distribution
*Almost all of sub-Saharan Africa and southern
Morocco*

Average size
2ft. 4in.-3ft.

Breeding details
*Difficult to find eggs small enough
to feed young snakes*

● Colubridae

Elaphe guttata guttata [Cornsnake]

Very popular throughout the USA, this
magnificent grass snake occurs in a
wide variety of habitats: rocky terrain,
woodland, prairies, pine forests and the
outskirts of farms where rodents are
legion. It is diurnal in spring but readily
switches to a nocturnal habit on warm
summer nights.

Distribution
Southern and eastern parts of the USA

Average size
4.5ft.

Breeding details
*The most popular snake in terrariums,
as much for its beauty as for its docile
nature and ease of rearing*

Boidae

Morelia viridis
[Green Tree Python]

Solitary and arboreal, this jewel of tropical virgin forests is a fascinating example of camouflage at work. Vivid cryptic coloration combined with a disconcerting ability to remain perfectly still together render it virtually invisible to predators while improving its efficiency as a hunter. It hunts mainly birds, small mammals and lizards.

Distribution
Irian Jaya, Papua New Guinea and the Yorke Peninsula in Southeastern Australia

Average size
4.5ft. (maximum 6.5ft.)

Breeding details
Popular in terrariums but remains expensive

Boidae

Python molurus molurus
[Indian Python]

Venerated in Indian temples the long Indian python is a denizen of humid jungles where it glides effortlessly over the uneven terrain despite its impressive girth. It may look indolent but it strikes at lightening speed, its powerful jaws seizing prey in a flash before the python squeezes it to death in 13 feet of scaly muscle.

Distribution
India, Bangladesh, Nepal, Pakistan, Sri Lanka

Average size
10ft. (maximum 15ft.)

Breeding details
Sadly, this species is often crossed with other varieties

Boidae

Python regius (melanistic)
[Ball Python]

This mutated Ball Python is barely recognizable as such. Only a handful exist in captivity worldwide, including a magnificent specimen in France at the "Ferme Tropicale" in Paris.

See page 97 for details of the Ball Python

Colubridae

Elaphe obsoleta lindheimeri f. *leucistic*
[Texas Rat Snake (leucistic)]

Snakes with a leucistic gene all have a milky, ivory-like sheen that enhances their natural beauty. The gene gives rise to deficient chromatophores (pigment cells) which affect pigmentation. All captive-bred leucistic snakes are directly descended from the original carrier for the gene, discovered in Texas some 30 years ago.

Distribution
USA from Louisiana to Texas

Average size
5ft.

Breeding details
Too nervous to be popular

Colubridae

Lampropeltis getulus getulus
[Eastern Kingsnake]

This vanishing species is increasingly under threat from intensive farming, sprawling urbanization and wanton deforestation. Faced with the continuing destruction of its biotopes, the Kingsnake is probably headed for extinction – especially since numbers bred in captivity are not sufficient to guarantee its survival.

Distribution
Eastern USA

Average size
5ft.

Breeding details
Unjustly neglected

Colubridae

Lampropeltis triangulum sinaloae
[Sinaloan Milk Snake]

This little gem of a snake, only discovered 20 years ago, lives in one of the most hostile environments of all: a desert region of blistering heat and drought where it only rains once a year. To survive in these extreme conditions, the Sinaloan Milk Snake has adapted to a nocturnal, fossorial lifestyle, feeding on lizards and rodents.

Distribution
Mexico

Average size
3ft.

Breeding details
One of the most common "fake corals"; reared in captivity much like the other species

● Colubridae

Pituophis melanoleucus mugitus
[Florida Pine Snake]

When disturbed, this snake from the Deep South puts on an impressive show of force, hissing very loudly while preparing to strike. Because it can hiss much louder than other snakes (using a fold of skin over the trachea), hissing is usually all it takes to scare off most intruders. Its massive build allows it to hunt substantial prey such as young rabbits.

Distribution
Florida, South Carolina and Alabama

Average size
5ft.

Breeding details
Popular with keepers despite its impetuous nature

● Colubridae

Psammophis sibilans [Short-snouted Grass Snake/African Beauty Racer]

This diurnal snake with its slightly flattened head shape has venomous rear fangs with which to dispatch lizards, its favorite prey. Extremely widely distributed, it has adapted remarkably well to a variety of different habitats ranging from Saharan desert environments to the tropical rain forests of Tanzania.

Distribution
Broadly distributed south of the Sahara, from Morocco to Tanzania

Average size
5ft. 3in.

● Colubridae

Rhamnophis (Thrasops) aethiopissa

Mimicking the appearance of a more dangerous species is a good way to be left in peace: this snake mimics the colors of the notoriously venomous Boomslang. Its relative, Jackson's Tree Snake, uses a similar strategy and both have similar lifestyles (although only the latter is arboreal).

Distribution
Virgin forests of Kenya, Tanzania, Uganda, Rwanda and Burundi

Average size
3-4ft.

● Viperidae

Atheris chlorechis
[Western Bush Viper]

This little viper has a short, prehensile tail and markings that are perfectly adapted to its strictly arboreal lifestyle. Predominantly leaf-green in color, sometimes with black spots, it is found in tropical and subtropical forests where it feeds off lizards and occasionally amphibians and small mammals. It also ventures into coffee plantations and this casual consorting with man has caused some serious accidents but few deaths. When threatened by a predator, this species is said to put up a terrific fight.

Distribution
Guinea to Nigeria

Average size
16in.

● Viperidae

Cerastes cerastes
[Desert Horned Viper]

Buried and immobile in the sand, the only sign of this discreet viper's presence are the two little horns above its eyes. Superbly adapted to the desert climate, it lies in wait for lizards that share its liking for the more clement nighttime temperatures. Its characteristic sideways gait - known as "sidewinding" - leaves telltale s-shaped tracks in the sand. The venom it produces is especially hematoxic and can cause cardiac arrest without emergency treatment.

Distribution
North Africa to the Middle East

Average size
2ft.

● Viperidae

Vipera aspis (melanistic)
[Asp Viper - melanistic]

This snake used to be regarded as a pest but it is actually highly efficient at limiting the rodent population. Widespread throughout southern Europe, it likes rocky scrub vegetation where it hunts by day except for the hottest days of the summer when it is nocturnal. It hibernates in winter using fat stored from spring to autumn. The Asp viper accounts for a large number of snakebites but very few deaths - only one a year in France, for example.

Distribution
Southeastern Europe and northern Spain

Average size
2ft.

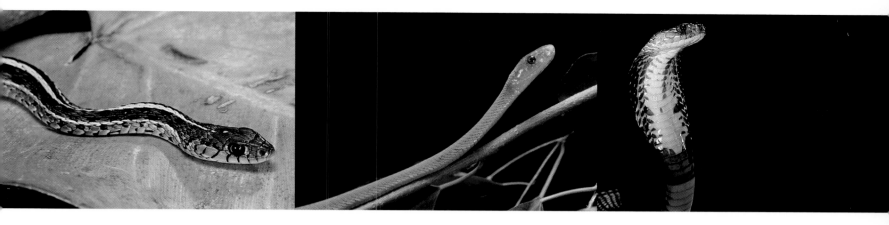

● Colubridae

Thamnophis sirtalis similis
[Bluestripe Garter Snake]

These Snakes – named after the blue
stripe running down their flanks –
huddle together in enormous numbers
in winter, sheltering quite deep
underground in cavities and crevices
until the spring. Seeing this seething
mass of reptilian flesh emerge from its
winter hiding place is a queasy sight ....
Their first task is to mate and find food
– fish and amphibians.

Distribution
Florida

Average size
3ft. 5in.

Breeding details
Prolific and popular

● Elapidae

Dendroaspis angusticeps
[Eastern Green Mamba]

Of all the venomous snakes, none so
effectively crystallizes popular phobias
as the Green Mamba. Documentaries
and films may have exaggerated its
macabre prowess but it is nonetheless
a formidable adversary. When
cornered this notorious reptile can
deliver bite after bite, injecting a virulent
neurotoxic venom that quickly causes
respiratory failure and can be fatal.
Victims have been known to die in a
matter of hours (five to 15). It is a keen
bird hunter, spending its life among the
branches where it slips easily and very
quickly from one nest to another.

Distribution
East Africa to South Africa

Average size
6ft.

● Elapidae

Naja siamensis
[Indo-Chinese Spitting Cobra]

This species causes many thousands
of deaths each year. It is a significant
risk in areas where a high proportion
of the population walks barefoot
across its territory - fatal accidents in
rice paddies, for example, are legion.
As with most snakebites by elapids,
the venom works by paralyzing the
respiratory system, causing
asphyxiation. When really incensed
by an intruder, this cobra can even
spit its venom. Renowned for its
voracious appetite, it hunts small
mammals, lizards, amphibians
and even other snakes.

Distribution
Southeast Asia

Average size
4ft.

● Viperidae

Agkistrodon bilineatus
[Common Cantil]

The young Common Cantil has a
special strategy to attract prey that
works with a great many amphibians,
small mammals and birds. It rolls into a
ball, wiggling the yellow tip of its tail to
mimic a caterpillar or worm. Adults
make less use of this tactic but are
nonetheless ferocious predators,
lurking invisibly in the debris of the
forest floor. This species lives near
water in tropical forests where man's
presence is rare. Snakebites are equally
rare therefore but always serious
without treatment.

Distribution
Mexico to Costa Rica

Average size
2ft. 7in.

● Viperidae

Agkistrodon contortrix
[Southern Copperhead]

Perfectly camouflaged amidst the dead
leaves by its cryptic coloring, the
copperhead ambushes its prey, biting
with lightening speed and devastating
efficiency - the victim soon collapses
and dies a few yards away from the
hemorrhagic venom. The Copperhead
will soon find its prey again even in this
tangled vegetation using its highly
developed sense of smell. One of its
habits is communal hibernation:
several dozen Copperheads hibernate
in the same place occasionally allowing
in different species (rattlesnakes and
grass snakes).

Distribution
Eastern half of the USA to northern Mexico

Average size
2ft. 3in.

● Viperidae

Trimeresurus purpureomaculatus
[Mangrove Pit Viper]

Only active by night, this rattlesnake
moves slowly and stealthily among
the branches, virtually invisible thanks
to its camouflage and controlled
movements. More massive than its
relative Trimeresurus albolabris, the
Mangrove Pit Viper likes rain forests
and mangrove swamps where it feeds
mainly on rodents, birds, amphibians
and lizards. Fatal encounters with this
snake are extremely rare although it
is known to be aggressive and
dangerous.

Distribution
*India, Bangladesh, Myanmar, Thailand,
Malaysia and Sumatra*

Average size
2ft. 7in.

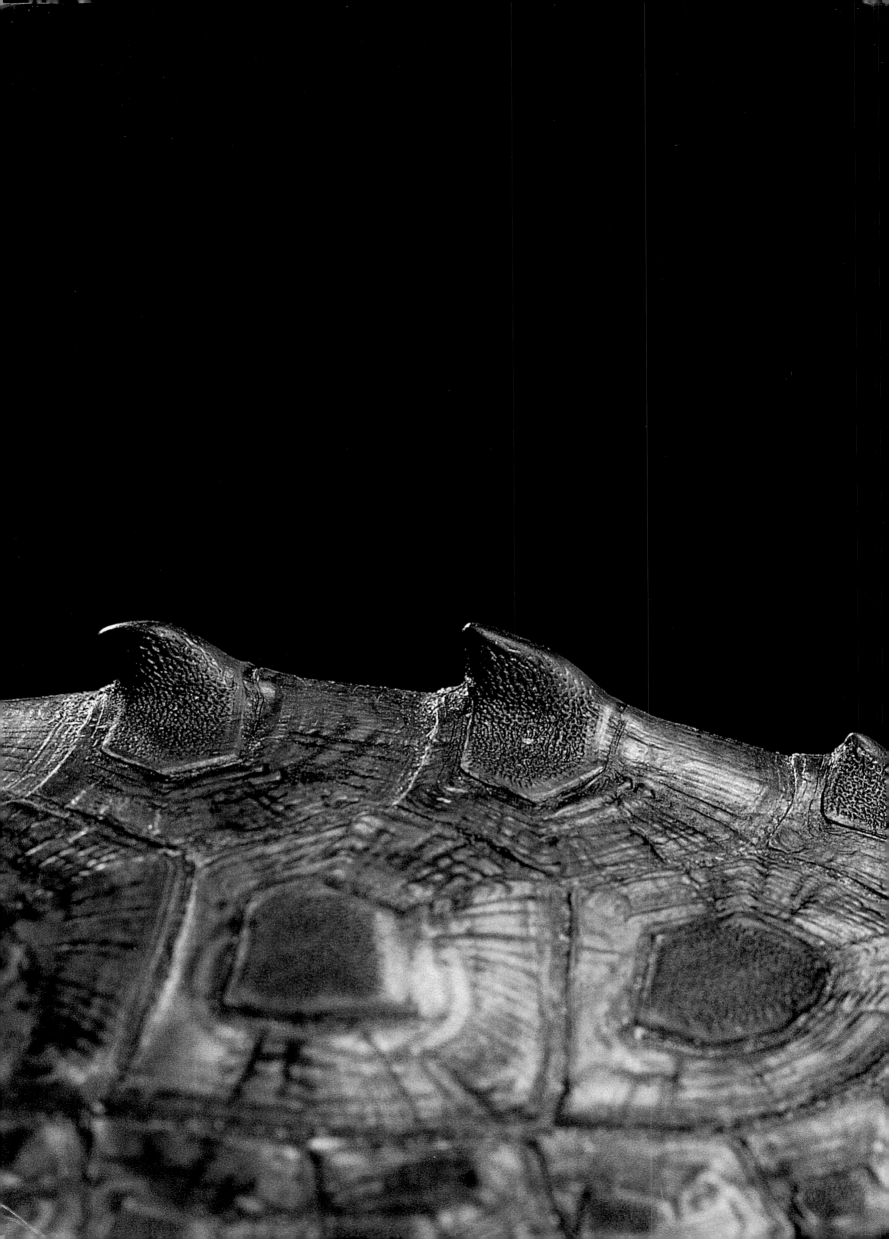

Turtles have always had a special place in the human heart who often forget that these non-slithering, non-venomous creatures are reptiles at all...

Directly descended from the oldest forms of reptile, turtles have evolved into two distinct groups that are distinguished by their method of neck retraction. Arch-necked turtles ("cryptodires"), which include terrestrial tortoises, marine turtles and some of the soft water turtles, retract their heads in an S-shaped curve. Side-necked turtles ("pleurodires"), which are aquatic turtles found only in the southern hemisphere (South America, Africa and Australasia) simply withdraw their heads sideways under the shell.

A turtle's shell is composed of bony plates that are knitted together to form an armor-like structure. These bones are covered with large horny shields of varying degrees of color called scutes. In some fresh water turtles and one marine turtle, this horny shield has been replaced in the course of evolution by smooth leathery skin. The shell is a living structure that forms an integral part of the turtle and grows with it. The spinal column and ribs are fused to the dorsal carapace; the lower ventral part of the shell is called the plastron.

Turtles have no teeth but their powerful jaws are covered by a horny, keratinized beak that varies in structure depending on diet: finely serrated for cutting grasses or extremely pointed for tearing flesh.

Males have an erectile penis and launch into elaborate courtship rituals before mating. Females are all oviparous, often laying their eggs in the sand and leaving them to be incubated by the sun. In most cases, the sex of the embryo is determined by the temperature of incubation rather than chromosomes. Hatchlings are independent from birth, which is just as well since they may take weeks to dig their way to the surface.

Turtle life-expectancy is truly remarkable: 20-50 years for aquatic turtles, 60-150 years for terrestrial tortoises and probably more than 200 years for the giant species. There are currently known to be more than 260 species of turtles living in every kind of habitat worldwide except for the most extreme regions.

● **Previous double-page display** *Graptemys nigrinoda* **Details page 160**
● **Left** *Heosemys spinosa* [Spiny Turtle] **Details page 152**

Aquatic turtles

For the 220 species of aquatic turtles (grouped into 11 families) the shell is not the only means of defense. Faster than their terrestrial cousins, they rely on speed and the ability to escape predators in the safety of the water. Adults are rarely captured but young turtles are easy prey for a brief, critical period until saved by rapid growth.

The females of large species that live in open environments, where the young are even more vulnerable, are prolific breeders.

Aquatic turtles are usually carnivorous and insectivorous but some large species, together with older members of the Emydidae family are herbivorous. Turtles frequently change their eating habits, even adapting the shape of the head with age. Aquatic turtles have separate digits that may or may not be webbed, depending on lifestyle. North American turtles have developed a remarkable adaptation to cope with hibernation: buried in mud at the bottom of the water, they slow their metabolism right down, absorbing water-borne oxygen through the skin by gaseous exchange. They can even survive the partial freezing of their non-vital organs with no adverse effects whatsoever.

This surprising little turtle has a circular carapace with sharp spines on the marginal scutes.

In adults these spines are mainly visible at the rear of the top shell. Mainly nocturnal, the Spiny Turtle lives in woodland zones within reach of water where it feeds on plants, fruit, earthworms, snails and other invertebrates.

Heosemys spinosa
[Spiny Turtle]

Family
Bataguridae

Distribution
Malaya, Indonesia

Average size
10–12in.

Breeding details
Attracts attention because of its strange appearance

Only leaving the water to bask daily in the sun or lay eggs, this small, strictly aquatic turtle has a characteristic roof-shaped carapace. Its home is the River Indus, its tributaries and the adjoining network of man-made canals. Extremely agile and fearful, it disappears into the water at the first sign of trouble. Its diet consists mainly of small invertebrates, snails, mollusks and aquatic plants.

Kachuga smithi
[Indian Roof Turtle]

Family
Bataguridae

Distribution
Pakistan

Average size
10in.

Breeding details
Wild, but easy to rear in captivity

This beautiful soft-shell turtle is the sole representative of its family. Its long cylindrically-shaped snout allows it to breathe at the surface of the water while keeping its body immersed. Adults are almost exclusively herbivorous, eating plants and windfalls from the trees that grow along their aquatic habitat. Despite its appearance, this species has nothing in common with marine turtles except for its mode of locomotion using mainly forelimb propulsion.

Carettochelys insculpta
[Fly River Turtle/Pig-nosed Turtle]

Family
Carettochelyidae

Distribution
Papua New Guinea, Cape Yorke in Southeastern Australia

Average size
16-20in.

Breeding details
Adults are known to fight — be warned!

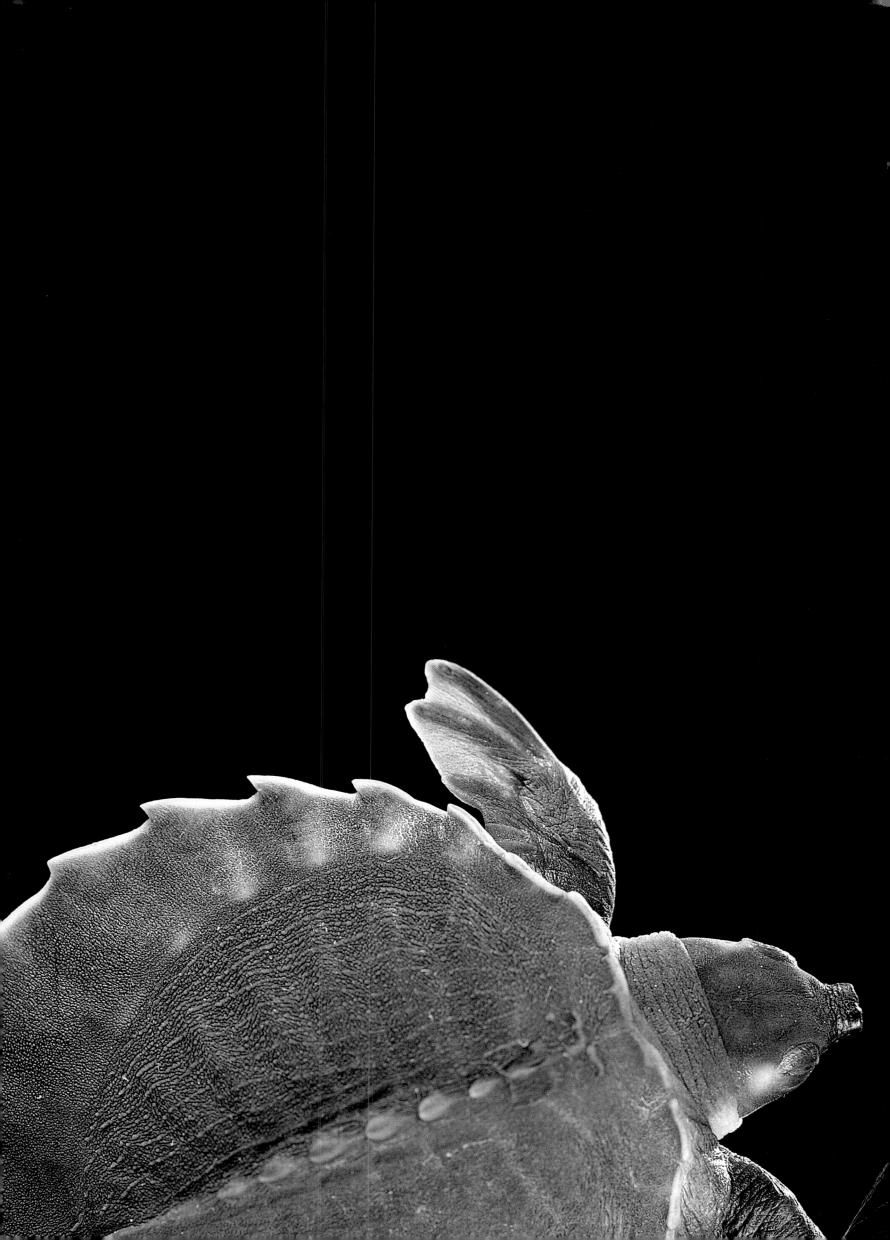

William's South American Side-necked Turtle is instantly recognizable from the face paint: black symmetrical markings running from the nostrils to the eyes and down to the neckline. Its favorite habitats are rivers, lakes and ponds rich with vegetation where it can hide among the plants. Its menu consists mainly of fish, snails and invertebrates, with a side helping of aquatic greens.

Phrynops williamsi
[William's South American Side-necked Turtle]

Family
Chelidae

Distribution
Southeastern Brazil, Uruguay

Average size
14in.

Breeding details
Very rare

The mischievous expression and fixed smile belong to a rare, shy species that looks extremely cramped in its shell – as if squashed by the small depression in the center of the dorsal carapace. This turtle likes shallow, marshy waters but after heavy rains will readily venture into the flooded savanna in search of its favorite food: frogs, tadpoles, fish, snails and aquatic invertebrates.

Acanthochelys spixii
[Spiny-neck Turtle]

Family
Chelidae

Distribution
Uruguay, Brazil

Average size
8in.

Breeding details
Regularly bred by a few committed keepers

Following double-page display ●

The meandering waterways of tropical forests are home to this powerful swimmer that only leaves the water to bask in the sun at the water's edge or on tree trunks. Groups of these turtles may be seen taking the sun together, ready to dive for cover at the least sign of danger. The species is omnivorous, feeding on small invertebrates and aquatic plants.

Emydura subglobosa
[Australian Red-bellied Short-necked Turtle]

Family
Chelidae

Distribution
Papua

Average size
8–12in.

Breeding details
This tropical tortoise has magnificent colorings and is the most easily bred in captivity

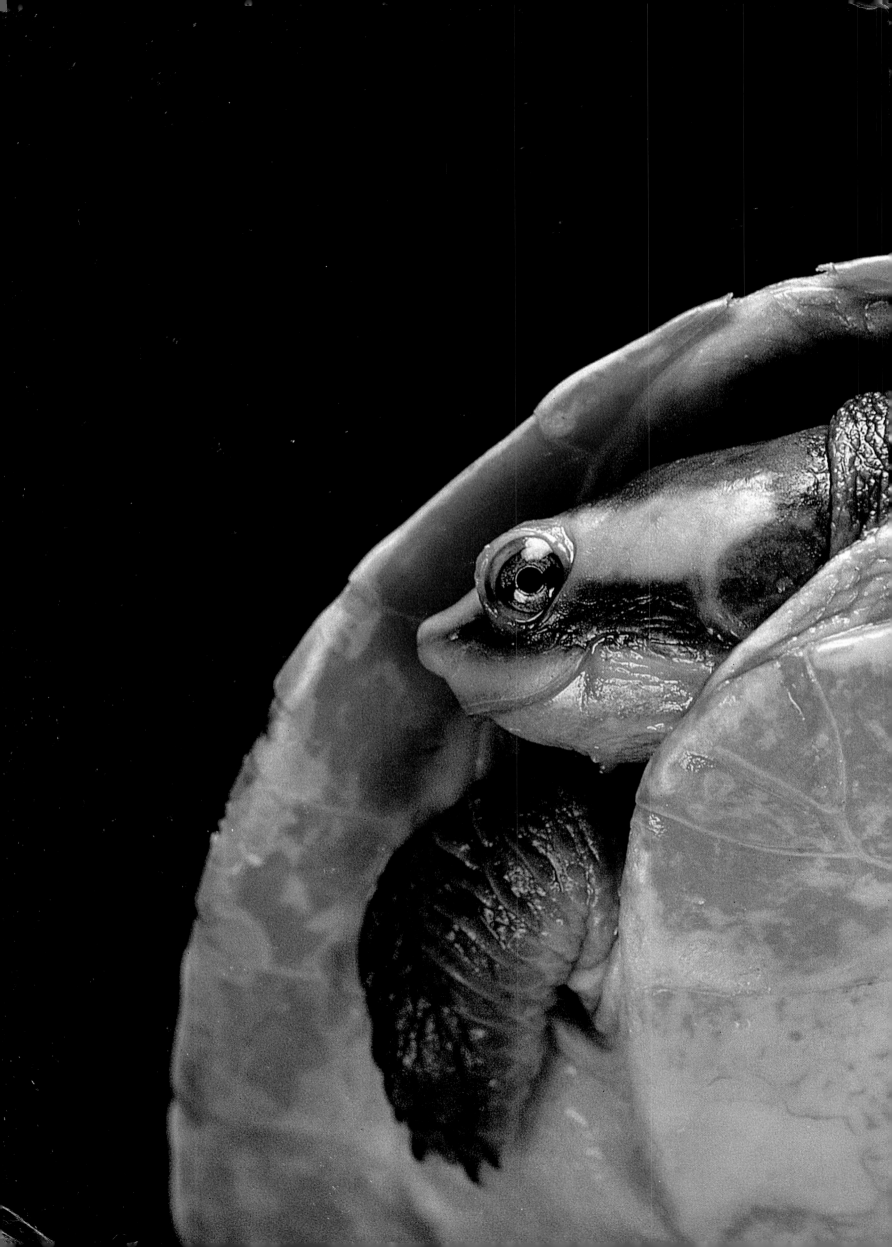

Opening double-page display ●

There are marked differences between the males and females of this species: females are larger than the males, generally vegetarian and fond of deep waters; males are more carnivorous and like shallow waters. (A similar pattern has been observed in other aquatic turtles.) This species also has distinctive mounds or ridges on the top of the carapace and decorative markings on the head.

Graptemys nigrinoda
[Northern Black-knob
Sawback Map Turtle]

Family
Emydidae
Distribution
USA
Average size
8–14in., depending on sex
Breeding details
*Occasionally reared on
specialized farms in the USA*

No ordinary aquatic turtle ●-------- **by any means this colossus is an implacable and formidable adversary.**
Despite its aquatic nature, it is a poor swimmer and prefers to walk along the riverbed. More surprising still is the technique it uses to entice victims into its merciless, snapping jaws. Lying motionless on the bottom, it gapes cavernously to reveal a small pink, worm-like lure at the back of its mouth, closing its jaws on unsuspecting prey in an instant.

Macroclemys temminckii
[Alligator Snapping Turtle]

Family
Chelydridae
Distribution
Southeastern USA
Average size
*16–20in. (females)
2ft. (males)*
Breeding details
Needs an outdoor environment

These pretty yellow dots on the carapace, head and limbs belong to the appropriately named Spotted Turtle, one of the best known and smallest of its family. It likes marshes and ditches where it feeds mainly on aquatic plants, insects and amphibians. During the cold months, it hibernates for several months in the mud, in thick plant debris or in tunnels belonging to aquatic rodents.

Clemmys guttata
[Spotted Turtle]

Family
Emydidae

Distribution
Eastern USA

Average size
8in.

Breeding details
Difficult to acclimatize but a good breeder once established

Following double-page display

The lovely Painted Turtle takes its name from the colorful designs on its carapace and limbs.
Males are smaller than females (like some other species) and use elaborate courtship behavior to woo their partner, stroking her nose repeatedly with their long front claws to encourage her to mate. This very common species likes calm waterways, lakes and rivers.

Chrysemys picta bellii
[Western Painted Turtle]

Family
Emydidae

Distribution
USA

Average size
7in. (males)
10in. (females)

Breeding details
Capable of surviving cold winters with no ill effects

Pages 166-167

A century of relentless hunting and the systematic destruction of its last remaining biotopes nearly drove this sweet-fleshed species to the verge of extinction. Happily, numbers have now stabilized since it was declared a protected species. Diamondback Terrapins are happiest in brackish waters, lagoons, marshes and estuaries where they feed on a wide variety of crustaceans, mollusks and aquatic plants.

Malaclemys terrapin centrata
[Diamondback Terrapin]

Family
Emydidae

Distribution
East Coast of the USA

Average size
8-12.5in.

Breeding details
At risk of disappearing from amateur collections due to lack of captive breeding

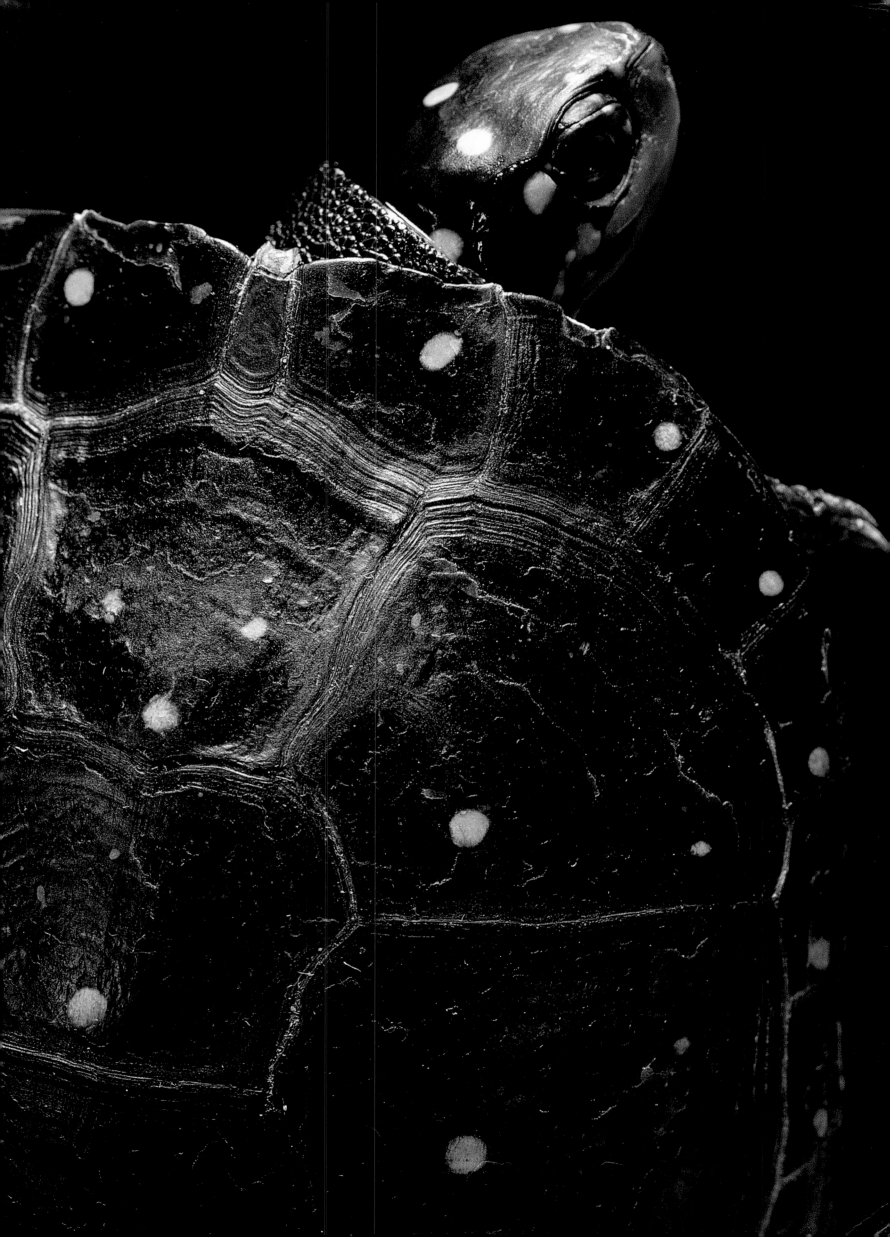

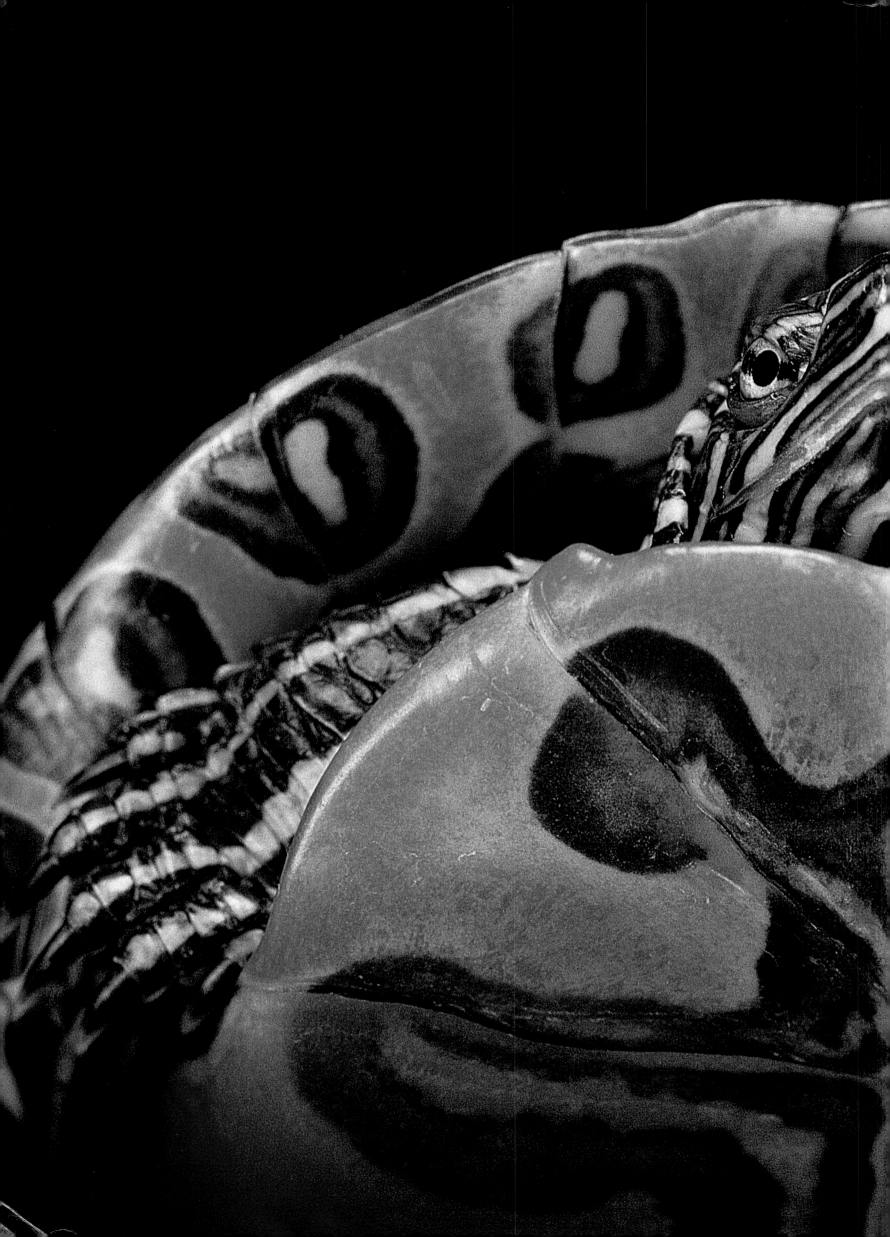

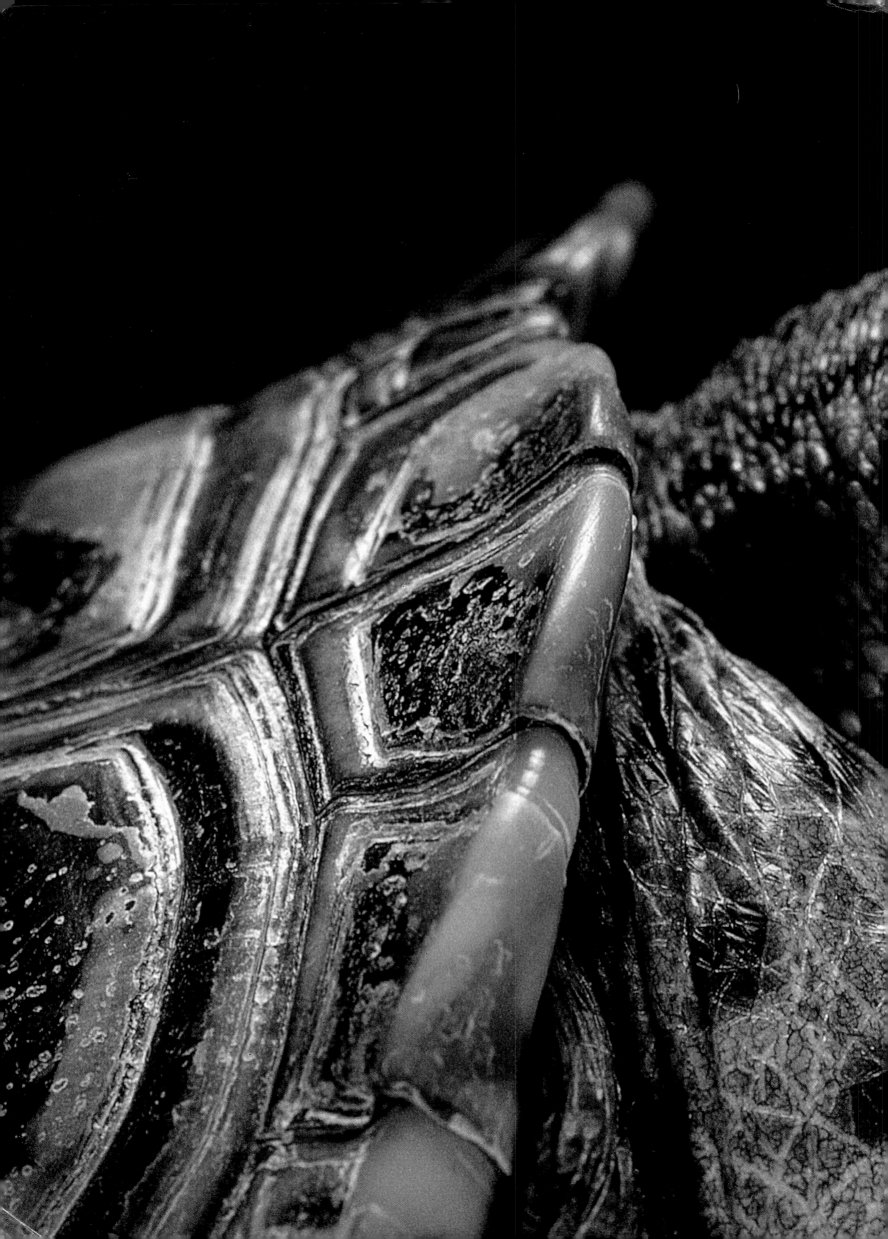

Stacked one on top of the other on tree trunks in full sun away from the shore, these very timid turtles cascade into the water at the least sign of danger. The False Map Turtle is larger than its relative (Graptemys nigrinoda) and shows a distinct preference for large bodies of water such as lakes, rivers and deep, slow-flowing waterways. It feeds on small vertebrates and invertebrates, mollusks and aquatic plants.

Graptemys pseudogeographica
[False Map Turtle]

Family
Emydidae

Distribution
USA

Average size
8–12.in.

Breeding details
Bred by the thousand to satisfy the demand for pets

Juveniles are masterpieces of eccentricity with their shells decorated with asymmetrical designs on a brightly colored background. Adult carapaces are less flamboyant but much more domed. This is the southernmost species of American turtle, separated from its close relatives by the Amazon Basin.

Trachemys dorbignyi
[South American Slider]

Family
Emydidae

Distribution
Southern Brazil, Uruguay, Paraguay

Average size
10–12in.

Breeding details
Too similar in appearance to the "Red Eared Slider" to attract attention

This species readily scours the wetlands of tropical forests

in search of marshes, waterholes and slow-flowing streams. It is nocturnal and keeps to a diet based on mollusks, a wide variety of small, water-borne prey and aquatic plants.

Kinosternum leucostomum
[White-lipped Mud Turtle]

Family
Kinosternidae

Distribution
Central America

Average size
5.5in.

Breeding details
Discreet and easily reared in captivity

Following double-page display

The pungent odor given off by its musk glands

keeps predators at bay. This rounded turtle with very primitive anatomical and biological characteristics flourishes in the Old World while its close relatives are found in the New World. It is equally happy in fast or slow-flowing waters where it burrows into the mud in the dry season and aestivates until the rains come.

Pelusios rhodesianus
[Variable Mud Turtle]

Family
Pelomedusidae

Distribution
Central and South Africa

Average size
10in.

Breeding details
Rarely captive bred

This species has exchanged a hard, scaly carapace for soft, leathery skin.

Being smoother and more flexible, it allows the turtle to move more easily along the muddy riverbed and swim faster in deep waters. Aggressive by nature, both partners inflict serious, permanent injuries on each other when mating.

Pelodiscus sinensis
[Chinese Soft Shell Turtle]

Family
Trionychidae

Distribution
China, Vietnam, Thailand

Average size
10in.

Breeding details
Widely bred for its flesh in Asia

Terrestrial tortoises

The term "Terrestrial Tortoises" refers exclusively to the 40 or so species of the family Testudinidae and does not include the so-called "aquatic" turtles that live predominantly in terrestrial habitats. The Testudinidae are found on every continent where the weather is suitable except for Australia.

The vast majority of terrestrial tortoises have a hemispherical carapace that is thought to have evolved as a defense against voracious carnivores. Predators may gnaw the edges of the carapace but in most cases they cannot get at the tender-fleshed tortoise inside.

To compensate for their weight, terrestrial tortoises have developed powerful legs with fused digits. When threatened, the legs and head are fully retracted into the carapace until the coast is clear – the predator having left or lost interest in a creature that has just turned itself into a living stone.

The Testudinidae have adapted remarkably well to many different environments including desert habitats, Mediterranean regions, woodlands, savanna and even rocks. They are predominantly herbivorous although some species are known to develop omnivorous eating habits.

The debonair Leopard Tortoise plods back and forth across its territory chewing large quantities of grass – until it too is devoured by any one of a number of predators, including lions. The eggs hold the record for incubation: up to 460 days. This characteristic savanna tortoise is very widely distributed, ranging from semi-arid to woodland environments.

Geochelone pardalis
[Leopard Tortoise]

Family
Testudinidae

Distribution
East Africa from the Sudan to South Africa

Average size
14–27in. (but very variable depending on geographic origin)

Breeding details
Choose captive-bred specimens in preference to those caught in the wild (which frequently pose problems)

This species is inactive for much of the year and only emerges from its burrows at the start of the rainy season. It will spend the next few months finding food, mating and laying eggs. Spider Tortoises are especially fond of young green shoots but in this arid region on the coast of Madagascar where food is scarce, zebu dung is not to be sniffed at either...

Pyxis arachnoides
[Malagasy Spider Tortoise]

Family
Testudinidae

Distribution
Southern Madagascar

Average size
7in.

Breeding details
Unjustly neglected by experienced keepers because of its very placid lifestyle

Following double-page display

Evolution has converted the bony carapace of the Galapagos Tortoise to a lighter-weight, honeycomb structure. One of the largest of the tortoises (up to 440lbs.) this fabulous colossus lives on wet and misty moorland plateaus where it has survived undisturbed for thousands of years until threatened by the introduction of non-endemic animals. At the start of the 21st century, like so many other species this relic faces an uncertain future.

Chelonoidis nigra
[Galapagos (giant) Tortoise]

Family
Testudinidae

Distribution
Galapagos Islands

Average size
3-4ft.

Breeding details
Extremely rare and restricted to a few praiseworthy zoological establishments

The young are born with a very domed carapace that flattens out with age. This unusual morphology is remarkably well adapted to arid and semi-arid, high-altitude habitats that are scattered with rock formations. The soft, flexible carapace allows the tortoise to slip into narrow crevices and wedge itself tightly between the rocks where it cannot be dislodged by predators.

Malacochersus tornieri
[African Pancake Tortoise; also known as the Soft-shelled Tortoise, Crevice Tortoise and Tornier's Tortoise]

Family
Testudinidae

Distribution
Kenya, Tanzania

Average size
7in.

Breeding details
Lays few eggs at a time but has a regular reproductive cycle

Few things can stop this four-legged bulldozer forged from the

desert sands – a miracle of adaptation to a hostile environment. The sturdy African Spurred Tortoise is certainly no stranger to steep, rocky terrain. Its powerful legs with over-developed scales are ideal for digging deep burrows (up to 16ft. deep) where it shelters from the fierce heat. Due to the shortage of available food, it is an opportunistic feeder and will eat dried grasses, shriveled shrubs or even animal feces.

Geochelone sulcata
[African Spurred Tortoise]

Family
Testudinidae

Distribution
A broad belt south of the Sahara

Average size
20–27.5in.

Breeding details
So easy going and prolific that it is now more common in captivity than in the wild

This is undoubtedly one of the most beautiful of the terrestrial tortoises.

It inhabits semi-arid environments where it leads a gregarious existence and may often be seen sheltering in the heat of the day under the shrubs and thorn bushes that make up the bulk of its diet. The flesh is regarded as a delicacy, and intensive hunting has reduced tortoise populations to alarming levels.

Geochelone radiata
[Radiated Tortoise]

Family
Testudinidae

Distribution
Southern Madagascar

Average size
16in.

Breeding details
A protected but much sought-after and easily reared species that will soon be widely available thanks to committed captive programs

Index

Acknowledgments

Paul Starosta would like to thank the following people for their patience: Gaëlle, Cédric, Jordy, Olivier and Pierre from « La Ferme Tropicale », In Paris, where most of the photographs in this book were taken. Also a big thank-you to Luc Fougeirol from « La Ferme aux Crocodiles » in Pierrelatte where all of the crocodiles were photographed and to Bernard Thorens of the « Vivarium d'Yvoire » where the venomous snakes were photographed.

Teddy Moncuit would like to express his warmest thanks to the many people whose efforts were invaluable in producing this book. First a special mention for his partner Gorrette Dos Santos who helped with proofing and corrections. His thanks also to Jordy Reynes for his precious insight into venomous snakes, to Cédric Bordes for making himself available and providing information on aquatic turtles and venomous snakes, and to all of the team at « La Ferme Tropicale » who put up with his lack of availability while this book was being written: Olivier Le Duc, Gaëlle Combret, Frédérique Stuber, Mïckaël M'Baye, Aurélie Zeyssolff and Bernardo Silva Freitas.

Karim Daoues wishes to thank his parents for allowing his all-consuming passion to take pride of place over his studies at an early age. His thanks also to all those who have shared in a great adventure and worked alongside him at « La Ferme Tropicale ». A particular word of thanks to Dr Lionel Schilliger for unfailing answers to a barrage of questions; to Luc and Eric Fougeirol, founders of « La Ferme aux Crocodiles », a magical place for an enthusiast like Karim; and to the following people for their help, advice and support: Philippe Magnan, Jean-Pierre Macé, Jean Garzoni, Roger Bour, Dominique Gentier, Jean-Jacques Lemelle and Alain Grondin.

The Translator wishes to thank Colin McCarthy at the Natural History Museum in London for his invaluable help with some of the more technical aspects of this translation.

La Ferme Tropicale, 54 rue Jenner, 75013 Paris
Tel. : 33 (0)1 45 84 24 36. Fax : 33 (0)1 45 84 25 69
Email : contact@lafermetropicale.com
www.lafermetropicale.com

Above young *Furcifer (Chamaeleo) oustaletti* **Details page 79**

- **Left of page 1** *Uroplatus sikorae* [Mossy Leaf-tailed gecko] **Details page 80**
- **Pages 2 and 3** *Cerastes cerastes* [Desert Horner Viper] **Details page 146**
- **Page 4** *Chelonoidis nigra* [Galapagos (giant) Tortoise] **Details page 176**
- **Page 6** *Hydrosaurus weberi* [Weber's Sail-fin Lizard] **Details page 78**
- **Page 8** *Sanzinia madagascariensis* [Madagascar Tree Boa] **Details page 102**
- **Below** *Furcifer (Chamaeleo) oustalett* [Oustalet's Chamaeleon] **Details page 79**
- **Opposite, right** *Acrantophis madagascariensis* [Madagascan Ground Boa] **Details page 144**
- **Back flyleaf** *Gavialis gangeticus* [Garial] **Details page 36**

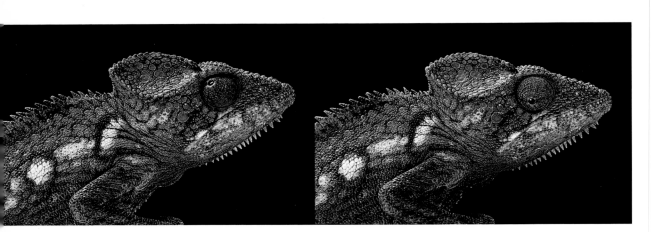

r**English language text translated from the French by Florence Brutton**

Editor Odile Perrard

Artistic Director Sabine Houplain

Creative Director Paul Starosta

Artwork Derek Westwood

Design and production Anne-Marie Bourgeois

Proofing Cécile Edrei

Photo-engraving Seleoffset, Turin, Italy
Printing Pollina, Luçon, France - n° L 86459-A

First published in France in 2002 by Editions du Chêne – Hachette Livre

Copyright © 2002, Editions du Chêne – Hachette Livre. All rights reserved.

This edition published by Barnes & Noble, Inc., by arrangement with Editions du Chêne – Hachette Livre.

2002 Barnes & Noble Books
M10987654321
ISBN 0-7607-3555-7

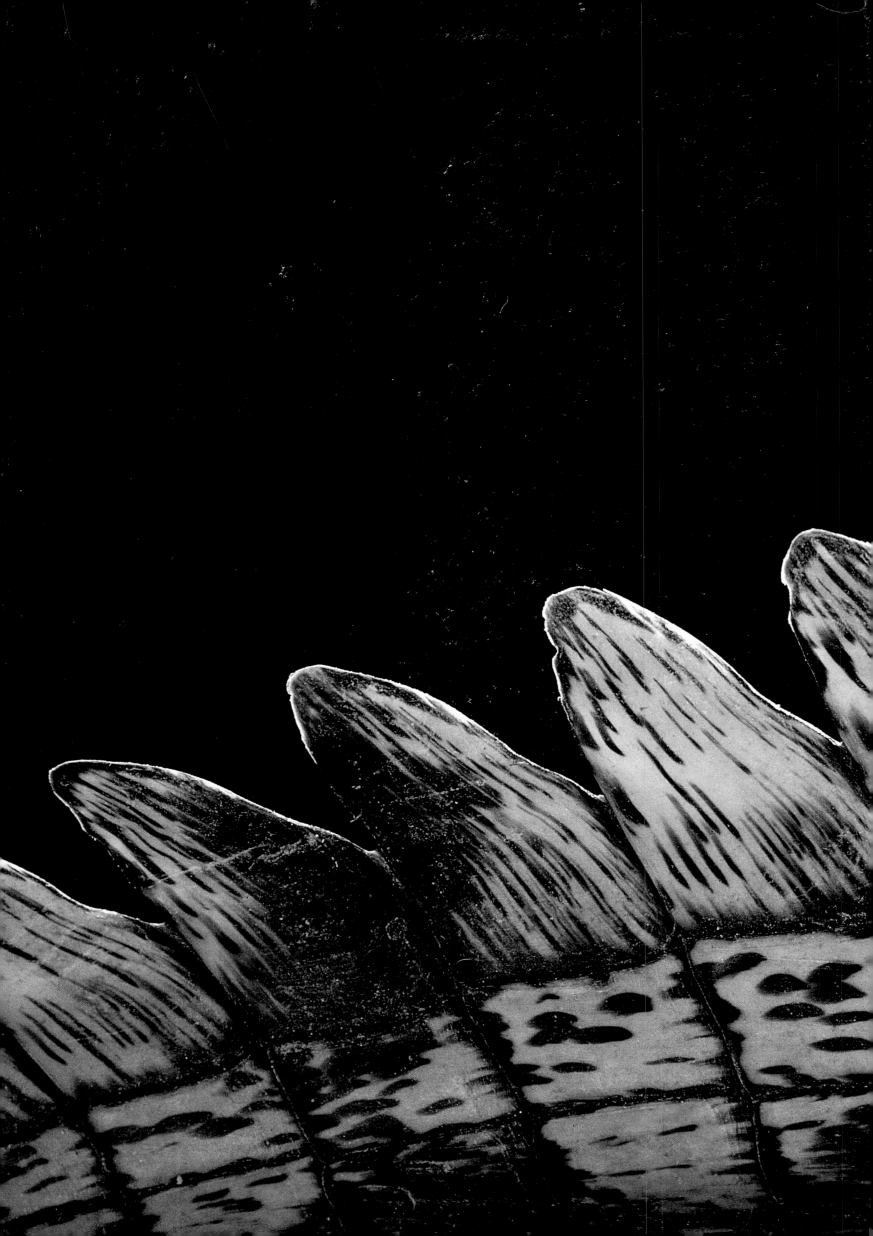